TINKLE
DOUBLE DIGEST

THE HURRICANE THAT HID IN A TREE

Script:
Rina Mukherjee
Illustrations:
V.B. Halbe

ON THE OUTSKIRTS OF A JUNGLE, LIVED AN OLD WOMAN WITH HER GRANDSON, CHANDU.

CHANDU GRAZED HIS SHEEP IN THE JUNGLE. ONE DAY—

SHEEP!

I'LL GRAB ONE WHEN THE BOY IS NOT LOOKING.

SUDDENLY—

CHANDU! OH, CHANDU!

COME HOME QUICKLY! THERE'S A HURRICANE COMING THIS WAY!

A HURRICANE!

3

BOTH THE OLD LADY AND THE BOY SEEM TO BE TERRIFIED. HURRICANE MUST BE A DEMON!

W- WHAT IF IT CATCHES ME!

AEEII... I'D BETTER HIDE SOMEWHERE.

I KNOW! I SHALL MINGLE WITH THE SHEEP AND HIDE IN THE SHEEPFOLD.

HURRY! HURRY!

GET IN, ALL OF YOU.

THE LEOPARD ENTERED THE BARN...

...AND WAS SHUT IN.

I'M SAFE HERE.

4

5

6

7

8

THE TERRIFIED BEAR PULLED FREE...

...LOST ITS BALANCE AND FELL.

IT'S TRULY A MONSTER!

YOU WERE RIGHT, BROTHER. IT IS AN AWFUL CREATURE.

DIDN'T I TELL YOU?

ER...IT MAY BE FOLLOWING ME!

LET'S RUN!

WAIT!

WHO'S CHASING YOU?

WE ARE FLEEING FROM HURRICANE.

HURRICANE! AND WHAT IS THAT?

OH, IT IS SIMPLY AWFUL! A CREATURE THAT DRAGS AND PULLS ANIMALS.

I MARVEL AT YOUR COWARDICE. WE JUNGLE FOLK SHOULD NEVER BE FRIGHTENED OF ANYONE.

COME, SHOW ME THE CREATURE!

THUMP!

HURRICANE HAS JUMPED ON MY BACK!

I'D BETTER RUN.

THE SOONER I REACH MY FRIENDS, THE BETTER... AH, THERE THEY ARE.

WHY, YOU COMPLETELY MISLED ME. IT IS NO DRAGGING OR TUGGING CREATURE AS YOU'D HAVE ME BELIEVE.

IT'S A RIDER OF BEASTS! WE'D BETTER NOT STAY HERE!

AND THE THREE ANIMALS RAN AWAY AS FAST AS THEY COULD.

12

The Priest's Assistant
An Indian Folktale

Script : Gayatri M Dutt
Illustrations : Ashok Dongre

A POOR PRIEST WAS ONCE CALLED TO A WEALTHY MAN'S HOUSE TO PERFORM A CEREMONY.

WIFE, I AM INDEED FORTUNATE!

THIS RICH MAN IS SURE TO PAY ME HANDSOMELY!

AT LEAST, I HOPE HE DOES.

WHY NOT SEND OUR SON IN ADVANCE, AS YOUR ASSISTANT.

A GOOD IDEA! IF THE RICH MAN THINKS I'M IMPORTANT ENOUGH TO HAVE AN ASSISTANT...

... HE MIGHT PAY ME MORE.

JUST THEN, THEIR SON CAME IN. THE PRIEST'S WIFE TOOK HER HUSBAND ASIDE.

YOU KNOW HOW FOOLISH OUR SON IS. YOU'D BETTER TELL HIM WHAT EXACTLY HE SHOULD DO.

13

SO THE PRIEST EXPLAINED HIS PLAN TO HIS SON. THEN—

...BUT MIND YOU, UNLIKE US THESE PEOPLE ARE RICH. THERE WILL BE CHAIRS AND TABLES AT THEIR HOUSE...

...SO BE SURE NOT TO SIT ON THE FLOOR. SIT ON A CHAIR, DO YOU HEAR?

SIT ON A CHAIR... A HIGH SEAT... A SEAT THAT IS HIGHER THAN THE GROUND. DO YOU UNDERSTAND?

OH, YES, YES, CERTAINLY!

AND TALK SENSIBLY AND ON IMPORTANT MATTERS.

WHAT?

HELP ME GOD!

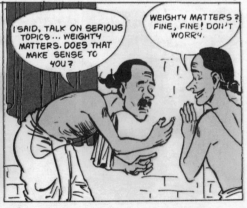

I SAID, TALK ON SERIOUS TOPICS... WEIGHTY MATTERS. DOES THAT MAKE SENSE TO YOU?

WEIGHTY MATTERS? FINE, FINE! DON'T WORRY.

SO WITH HIS FATHER'S ADVICE IN MIND, THE YOUTH SET OFF AND SOON ARRIVED AT THE RICH MAN'S HOUSE.

HE MUST BE THE PRIEST'S ASSISTANT.

HE WAS GIVEN A WARM WELCOME—

COME, PLEASE TAKE A SEAT.

SHE'S OFFERING ME A MAT TO SIT ON. BUT FATHER SAID...

THE YOUNG PRIEST LOOKED THIS WAY AND THAT...

...AND THEN MADE STRAIGHT FOR THE COW-SHED IN THE COURTYARD.

DONE IT! AND NOW I MUST TALK ABOUT HEAVY THINGS!

16

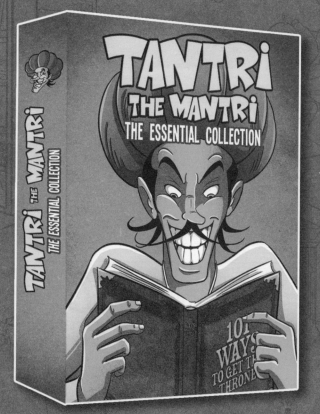

KALU AND HIS WIFE, JAMNA LIVED IN THE DEEP FOREST, FAR FROM CIVILIZATION.

WE HAVE COLLECTED A LOT OF HONEY THIS SUMMER

I'LL GO TO THE TOWN TOMORROW AND SELL IT.

SO EARLY NEXT MORNING —

TAKE GOOD CARE OF YOURSELF AND GET BACK BEFORE IT GETS DARK.

KALU SOLD THE HONEY IN THE TOWN AND BOUGHT A LOT OF THINGS WITH THE MONEY.

AT ONE OF THE SHOPS —

YOU ARE A GOOD CUSTOMER, KALU! HERE IS A SPECIAL GIFT FOR YOU!

OH! THANK YOU!

WHEN KALU REACHED HOME, HE GAVE JAMNA ALL THAT HE HAD BROUGHT FOR HER.

OOH! BANGLES! EAR-RINGS! HOW BEAUTIFUL THEY ARE!

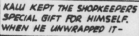

IT IS A PICTURE OF MY FATHER!

EVERY DAY THEREAFTER—

BLESS ME, FATHER! MAY ALL GO WELL TODAY.

HE GOES TO THAT CORNER EVERY MORNING! I WONDER WHAT HE'S GOT THERE!

JAMNA DECIDED TO INVESTIGATE.

OH! NO WONDER HE HIDES IT FROM ME!

THAT EVENING WHEN KALU CAME HOME AND GOT READY TO EAT—

I HAVE NOT COOKED FOR YOU TODAY AND WILL NEVER COOK FOR YOU AGAIN!

THE MIRROR BECAME THEIR MOST PRIZED POSSESSION.

THE FISHERMAN AND HIS DAUGHTERS

A Folktale from Kerala

Script:
Gayatri M. Dutt

Illustrations:
Ram Waeerkar

ONCE A POOR FISHERMAN DECIDED TO VISIT ONE OF HIS DAUGHTERS.

WELCOME, FATHER.

HOW ARE YOU, DEAR CHILD?

NICE PLACE YOU HAVE HERE.

I'M GLAD YOU LIKE IT, FATHER... COME, DINNER IS ALMOST READY.

THE FISHERMAN HAD A DINNER OF FISH AND TAPIOCA.

YOU ARE A GOOD COOK, MY CHILD. I MUST TELL YOUR MOTHER.

LATER—

HERE IS YOUR MAT, FATHER.

AH! NOW I SHALL SLEEP LIKE A LOG TILL MORNING.

AFTER A HAPPY STAY, THE FISHERMAN RETURNED HOME.

WIFE, WE NEED HAVE NO WORRIES. WE HAVE GIVEN OUR DAUGHTER INTO A GOOD FAMILY.

SOME DAYS AFTER THIS, THE FISHERMAN WENT TO SEE HIS YOUNGER DAUGHTER WHO WAS MARRIED TO A RICH MAN. HE REACHED THERE EARLY IN THE MORNING.

MY CHILD!

FATHER! I'M SO HAPPY TO SEE YOU!

PLEASE SIT DOWN. I'LL GET YOU WATER TO WASH.

HERE IS WATER, FATHER, AND SOME TOOTHPOWDER. YOU'LL FEEL FRESHER AFTER USING IT.

TOOTH-POWDER? WHAT'S THIS FOR?

SMELLS GOOD. I SUPPOSE IT TASTES GOOD TOO!

22

OHHH... KHACK KHACK ... KHACK, KHACK, KHACK...

LATER, AT LUNCH TIME —

...KHACK, KHACK...

COME, SIR. PLEASE SIT DOWN.

FATHER, PUT YOUR LEGS DOWN...

UH... OH... YES.

I MADE THESE DISHES SPECIALLY FOR YOU, FATHER.

AH!

23

24

THE NEXT MORNING—

FATHER, DID YOU SLEEP WELL?

I...I...OOOH ...I DID, MY CHILD.

OH! THE MOSQUITO NET! WHAT HAPPENED TO IT?

I... I...

I'LL MEND IT QUICKLY BEFORE THE HOUSEHOLD WAKES UP.

THAT VERY MORNING, THE FISHERMAN RETURNED HOME.

WIFE, YOU CANNOT IMAGINE THE PLIGHT OF OUR YOUNGER DAUGHTER! THE FOOD AT HER HUSBAND'S HOUSE IS QUITE UNHEALTHY. IT HAS GIVEN ME A TUMMY-ACHE!

BUT WORST OF ALL WAS THE HIGH JUMP I HAD TO TAKE IN THE NIGHT. THAT WAS TOO MUCH!

I DECIDED TO RETURN HOME AT ONCE. ONE MORE NIGHT THERE, AND I'D HAVE SURELY BROKEN ALL MY BONES!

THE SHOW-OFF

Readers' Choice

Illustrations: Ram Waeerkar

Based on a story sent by Ajay Pahuja

ONCE THERE WAS A RICH MAN WHO COULD NOT HELP SHOWING OFF.

THIS CUCKOO CLOCK IS FROM SWITZERLAND.

THIS IS A JAPANESE DOLL.

HOW NICE, BUT DO YOU HAVE A TALKING PARROT?

MY FRIEND HAS A TALKING PARROT.

A TALKING PARROT? I'LL GET ONE IMMEDIATELY! WAIT FOR ME...

AND OFF HE WENT TO THE MARKET-PLACE.

CAN THIS PARROT TALK?

THERE'S NO DOUBT ABOUT IT!

HERE'S A HUNDRED RUPEES FOR THIS PARROT.

!

27

28

NO NESTS IN THIS TREE.

NO HARM IN PROPPING THE LADDER UP, I SUPPOSE.

THERE YOU ARE!

STEADY, THERE! STEADY!

?

WHY IS HE CLIMBING THAT TREE?

KALIA!

HE'S...ER... GATHERING BERRIES.

HOW NICE.

BUT THERE ARE NO BERRIES ON THAT TREE!

I'VE A FEELING HE'S TRYING TO GET TO MOTHER HORNBILL'S NEST...

31

THE TRICK THAT FAILED

READERS' CHOICE

Based on a story sent by Ken

Illustrations: V.B. Halbe

OH, DEAR! HERE HE COMES!

AND JUST WHEN WE WERE GETTING READY TO EAT.

HELLO, MY FRIENDS. HOW ARE YOU TODAY?

COME IN, COME IN.

IF YOU MUST.

WILL YOU SHARE OUR LUNCH?

THANK YOU, I DON'T MIND IF I DO.

DOES HE EVER SAY NO?

LATER—

HE COMES EVERY DAY, TWICE A DAY, AND ONLY FOR FOOD. WE MUST DO SOMETHING.

YES, BUT WHAT?

I HAVE IT! LISTEN...

THE SAME EVENING—

HERE HE COMES!

HOW DARE YOU SPEAK TO ME LIKE THAT!

34

THE CITY LOVER

READERS' CHOICE

Based on a story sent by Hemal Parikh

Illustrations: Ram Waeerkar

KISAN! YOU HAVE COME BACK!

SO HOW ARE THINGS IN THE CITY?

WONDERFUL! JUST WONDERFUL!

IT MUST BE SOMEWHAT DIFFERENT FROM OUR VILLAGE.

SOMEWHAT? HEH! EVERYTHING IS BETTER IN THE CITY!

OH! UMM... WILL YOU HAVE A CUP OF TEA?

I DON'T MIND.

YOU SHOULD TASTE THE TEA IN THE CITY — IT IS MARVELLOUS!

REALLY?

FLOWERS, BIRDS, TREES — EVERYTHING IS FANTASTIC IN THE CITY!

LOOK AT THE FULL MOON, KISAN! ISN'T IT BEAUTIFUL!

NOT AS BEAUTIFUL AS THE MOON OVER THE CITY!

YOU FOOL! THE MOON IS THE SAME EVERYWHERE!

SLAP!

I HARDLY FELT THAT SLAP! YOU GET BETTER SLAPS IN THE CITY...!

BAH!

THE SUN

Script: J.D. Isloor

Illustrations: Anand Mande

YOU CAN SEE SEVERAL STARS IN THE SKY AT NIGHT...

...BUT IN THE DAYTIME, THE ONLY STAR YOU CAN SEE IS THE SUN.

IF THE SUN IS A STAR WHY DOESN'T IT LOOK LIKE OTHER STARS? WHY DOES IT LOOK LIKE A HUGE RED BALL? THE SUN LOOKS DIFFERENT FROM OTHER STARS BECAUSE IT IS MILLIONS OF TIMES CLOSER TO EARTH THAN ANY OTHER STAR. IF OUR SUN WERE AS FAR AWAY AS THE OTHER STARS, IT TOO, WOULD HAVE APPEARED TO US AS A TWINKLING SPECK IN THE SKY.

AFTER THE SUN THE NEXT CLOSEST STAR IS PROXIMA CENTAURI.

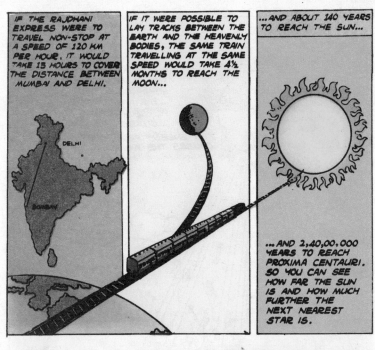

IF THE RAJDHANI EXPRESS WERE TO TRAVEL NON-STOP AT A SPEED OF 120 KM PER HOUR, IT WOULD TAKE 13 HOURS TO COVER THE DISTANCE BETWEEN MUMBAI AND DELHI.

DELHI

BOMBAY

IF IT WERE POSSIBLE TO LAY TRACKS BETWEEN THE EARTH AND THE HEAVENLY BODIES, THE SAME TRAIN TRAVELLING AT THE SAME SPEED WOULD TAKE 4½ MONTHS TO REACH THE MOON...

...AND ABOUT 140 YEARS TO REACH THE SUN...

...AND 2,40,00,000 YEARS TO REACH PROXIMA CENTAURI. SO YOU CAN SEE HOW FAR THE SUN IS AND HOW MUCH FURTHER THE NEXT NEAREST STAR IS.

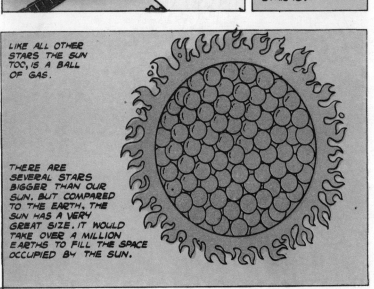

LIKE ALL OTHER STARS THE SUN TOO, IS A BALL OF GAS.

THERE ARE SEVERAL STARS BIGGER THAN OUR SUN. BUT COMPARED TO THE EARTH, THE SUN HAS A VERY GREAT SIZE. IT WOULD TAKE OVER A MILLION EARTHS TO FILL THE SPACE OCCUPIED BY THE SUN.

THE SUN IS THE SOURCE OF ALL ENERGY ON EARTH.
THE ENERGY FROM THE SUN CAUSES THE WINDS...
...THE WAVES AND CURRENTS OF THE OCEANS...
...CLOUDS AND RAIN AND SNOW.

IF THE SUN WERE TO STOP SHINING ALL LIVING THINGS ON EARTH, INCLUDING MAN, WOULD DIE OF COLD AND HUNGER.

COAL

IT IS VERY HOT IN MAY.

THE TEMPERATURE AT THIS TIME IS BETWEEN 35°C AND 40°C.

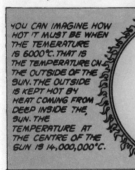

YOU CAN IMAGINE HOW HOT IT MUST BE WHEN THE TEMERATURE IS 6000°C. THAT IS THE TEMPERATURE ON THE OUTSIDE OF THE SUN. THE OUTSIDE IS KEPT HOT BY HEAT COMING FROM DEEP INSIDE THE SUN. THE TEMPERATURE AT THE CENTRE OF THE SUN IS 14,000,000°C.

YOU MAY NOT BELIEVE IT, BUT THAT RAY OF LIGHT COMING IN THROUGH YOUR WINDOW WAS FORMED IN THE CENTRE OF THE SUN THOUSANDS OF YEARS AGO.

IT TOOK SO LONG TO REACH THE EARTH BECAUSE IT HAD A HARD TIME COMING TO THE SURFACE OF THE SUN. IT KEPT BUMPING INTO GAS PARTICLES AND HAD TO ZIG-ZAG INSIDE THE SUN FOR CENTURIES AND CENTURIES. FINALLY IT MANAGED TO ESCAPE TO THE SURFACE AND RACED TO THE EARTH. IT TOOK ABOUT EIGHT MINUTES TO COVER THE DISTANCE BETWEEN THE SURFACE OF THE SUN AND YOUR WINDOW.

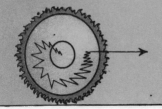

BESIDES LIGHT, THE SUN GIVES OFF SOME HARMFUL RAYS TOO. FORTUNATELY FOR US, OUR ATMOSPHERE, WHICH IS LIKE A PROTECTIVE BLANKET COVERING THE EARTH, ABSORBS THESE DANGEROUS RAYS AND PREVENTS THEM FROM REACHING US.

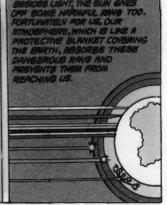

THE SUN'S SURFACE IS CONTINUALLY IN MOTION AND TONGUES OF FLAME LEAP OUTWARDS. THESE TONGUES OF FLAME ARE CALLED PROMINENCES. THEY ARE REALLY VISIBLE ONLY DURING AN ECLIPSE. SOMETIMES THESE PROMINENCES REACH OUT THOUSANDS OF KILOMETRES INTO SPACE.

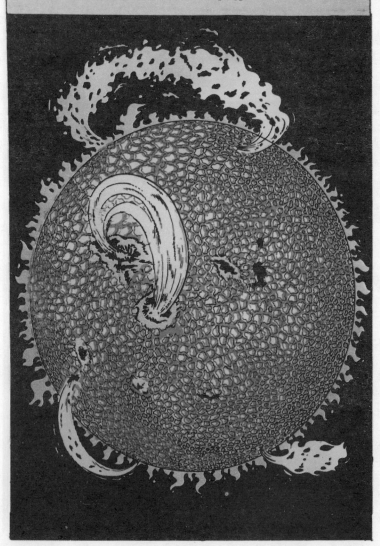

DISTURBANCES ON THE SUN CAN AFFECT THE EARTH TOO. ON 12TH NOVEMBER, 1960 THERE WAS A GREAT EXPLOSION ON THE SUN. SIX HOURS LATER A GIGANTIC CLOUD OF HYDROGEN GAS FLYING OUT FROM THE SUN, COLLIDED WITH THE EARTH AT A SPEED OF ABOUT 6400 KM A SECOND.

FOR HOURS ALL LONG-DISTANCE RADIO COMMUNICATIONS WERE BLACKED OUT.

...COMPASS NEEDLES WENT HAYWIRE.

AEROPLANE PILOTS LOST CONTACT WITH THEIR GROUND STATIONS ...

IN SOME PARTS OF THE WORLD ELECTRIC LIGHTS FLICKERED AS IF IN A STORM. YET THE AIR AND SKY WERE CLEAR AND SILENT. SOME OF THE DISTURBANCES LASTED FOR MORE THAN A WEEK!

This story by Ms Sadhana Vemuganti won the Third Prize in the Tinkle Original Story Competition

THE MAN WHO SOLD HIS MOUSTACHE

Illustrations: Ram Waeerkar

ONE EVENING, A YOUNG MAN GOT DOWN AT SITAPUR STATION.

IT WAS RAMU, THE NEW HEAD-MASTER OF THE VILLAGE SCHOOL.

RAMU WAS LOOKING FORWARD TO HIS JOB.

WHAT A LOVELY PLACE THIS IS!

ON REACHING THE SCHOOL BUILDING, HE OPENED THE DOOR OF A CLASSROOM AND—

WHAT... WHAT ON EARTH IS THIS?

HAVE I COME TO THE WRONG PLACE?

THE NEXT MORNING, RAMU MADE ENQUIRIES.

YES, RAMBABU. THE SCHOOL ROOMS HAVE BEEN USED AS COW-SHEDS FOR SEVERAL MONTHS.

AND THE CHILDREN DO THEIR LESSONS OUT OF DOORS? I'VE NEVER HEARD OF SUCH A...

...OH!

42

THIS IS RIDICULOUS, VEEPESHAMJI. I'M GOING TO DO SOMETHING ABOUT THIS!

RAMBABU, I HAVE BEEN A MASTER IN THIS SCHOOL FOR MANY YEARS. TAKE MY ADVICE LET THINGS BE AS THEY ARE

WHAT! BUT WHY?

THESE COWS BELONG TO THE ZAMINDAR OF OUR VILLAGE. IF ANYONE PROTESTS ABOUT THE USE THESE CLASSROOMS HAVE BEEN PUT TO...

... MALLUDADA IS SENT TO HANDLE THEM.

WHO IS MALLUDADA?

THE VILLAGE PEHALWAN! THE ZAMINDAR HAS KEPT HIM IN HIS SERVICE TO DO ALL HIS DIRTY JOBS.

WHEN THE PREVIOUS HEAD MASTER TRIED TO CLEAR THE CLASSROOMS OF THE COWS, MALLU BEAT HIM UP SO BADLY THAT THE POOR MAN LEFT THE VILLAGE THE VERY NEXT DAY.

MALLUDADA IS CRUEL AND UNJUST. BEWARE OF HIM!

THAT EVENING RAMU WAS WATCHING THE BUSY STREET SCENE...

45

46

BUT I'M IN SCHOOL BY THEN THAT'S WHY I HAVE COME NOW!

SO RAMU GOT TO WORK...

OUCH! OUCH! WHY ARE YOU PULLING SO HARD?

SO IT BEGAN, SO IT CONTINUED— THREE TIMES A DAY; EVERY DAY IN THE MORNING, DURING RAMU'S LUNCH BREAK AND AT NIGHT.

OOOOH! OUCH! GO EASY, WILL YOU, FOR HEAVEN'S SAKE?

A TIME CAME WHEN THE MOMENT HE SAW THE SLIM RAMU, THE HUGE PEHALWAN ACTUALLY BEGAN TO SHIVER.

OH, MY GOD! IT'S HIM AGAIN!

SOON, THE DASSERA FESTIVAL ARRIVED. A WRESTLING MATCH WAS HELD EVERY YEAR AT THIS TIME MALLUDADA WAS BUSY GETTING HIMSELF INTO SHAPE FOR IT.

I'VE WON IT!.. HUP! ... FOR THE PAST FOUR YEARS ... HUP!... AND I'LL WIN IT AGAIN.

JUST BEFORE THE MATCH, RAMU ARRIVED AS USUAL AND DID A FINE JOB ON HIS MOUSTACHE.

DOESN'T IT LOOK EXTRA FINE TODAY?

IT... OOOH!.. DOES! GROAN!

THEN RAMU SMILED WIDER THAN EVER AND PULLED SOMETHING OUT OF HIS POCKET.

NOW SIT STILL, WHILE I PUT ON THE FINISHING TOUCH.

EEEK! NO! PLEASE, NOT THAT!

BUT RAMU WAS ADAMANT. HE EVEN THREATENED MALLUDADA THAT HE WOULD TAKE HIM TO THE COURT AND FINALLY, HE HAD HIS WAY!

WHEN MALLUDADA ARRIVED AT THE MATCH GROUNDS, THE LARGE AUDIENCE THAT HAD GATHERED AND HARI, THE WRESTLER FROM THE NEXT VILLAGE —ALL STARED AT HIM.

THEN —

HA, HA. HA!

HO, HO. HO!

HAP, HAR, HAR!

STOP IT, DO YOU HEAR ME ?

BUT NOBODY WAS AFRAID OF MALLUDADA THAT EVENING ...

... HE LOOKS STRAIGHT OUT OF A CARTOON! HA, HA!

HA, HA HA!

THE MATCH BEGAN. BUT THE RIBBONS HAD BROKEN MALLUDADA'S WILL TO WIN. KNOWING THIS, HARI FOUGHT LIKE A TIGER...

... AND SOON —

CRASH!

48

HURRAH! OUR HARI WINS THE PRIZE OF RS 100 HURRAH!

THAT NIGHT, AT THE STROKE OF MIDNIGHT, RAMU CAME TO MALLUDADA'S HOUSE

I HAVE COME TO REMOVE THE RIBBONS

RAMU'S EYES SEEMED TO BE GLITTERING STRANGELY.

I'VE ALSO BROUGHT A SPECIAL OIL TO RUB IT WITH... KEROSENE!

WHAT! OH, NO!

YOU DON'T KNOW HOW BENEFICIAL KEROSENE IS TO THE HEALTH OF A MOUSTACHE. SIT STILL!

AND RAMU MASSAGED THE MOUSTACHE VIGOROUSLY.

OOOH! OUCH!

AND NOW...!

... I'M GOING TO SET FIRE TO MY MOUSTACHE. I DON'T WANT IT ANYMORE.

...RAMU'S VOICE ROSE TO A FEARFUL SHOUT...

HELP! HELP!

...AND MALLUDADA RAN FOR HIS LIFE...

I'LL MAKE A BONFIRE OUT OF MY MOUSTACHE. COME HERE, HA, HA, HA!

NOOO... MA, MA, HE IS BURNING MY MOUSTACHE...

THE COMMOTION WOKE THE NEIGHBOURHOOD AND A CROWD SOON SURROUNDED THE TWO MEN.

RAMBABU, I BEG YOU—TAKE BACK YOUR MONEY, BUT DON'T BURN MY MOUSTACHE!

IT IS MY MOUSTACHE. I FEEL LIKE BURNING IT.

THE VILLAGERS WHOM MALLUDADA HAD TERRORISED FOR SO LONG, BEGAN TO ACTUALLY FEEL SORRY FOR HIM.

RAMBABU, I'LL BE YOUR SLAVE FOR LIFE. I'LL DO ANYTHING YOU WANT ME TO DO, BUT DON'T HUMILIATE ME ANY FURTHER.

YES, RAMBABU TAKE BACK YOUR MONEY AND LEAVE HIM ALONE.

RAMU GAZED AT MALLUDADA

DID YOU SAY YOU WOULD DO ANYTHING I WANT YOU TO?

YES, YES...

ALL RIGHT, THEN GET YOUR COWS OUT OF THE SCHOOL.

AND CLEAN UP THE PLACE!

I'LL DO IT. I'LL DO IT.

DO IT NOW!

AND SO MALLU TOOK HIS COWS OUT OF THE SCHOOL BUILDING...

... AND CLEANED IT UP.

AFTERWARDS—

NOW PLEASE, PLEASE LET ME BUY MY MOUSTACHE BACK!

HERE'S YOUR MONEY I'LL NEVER TROUBLE YOU AGAIN...

OR THE VILLAGERS EITHER?

... OR THE VILLAGERS EITHER.

SOLD!

AND SO IT WAS THAT THE CHILDREN OF SITAPUR GOT BACK THE USE OF THEIR SCHOOL...

... AND THE PEOPLE OF SITAPUR, THEIR PEACE OF MIND.

Blessings of the Goddess

Story & Script :
Dev Nadkarni

Illustrations :
Ram Waeerkar

CHANDRAPUR WAS A PROSPEROUS KINGDOM, BUT—

SHAYANPUR IS THE ONLY VILLAGE THAT CONTRIBUTES NOTHING TO OUR ECONOMY.

OH, THAT VILLAGE IS FULL OF THE LAZIEST PEOPLE I'VE EVER COME ACROSS.

...AND THEY'RE AS SUPERSTITIOUS AS THEY'RE LAZY.

SUPERSTITIOUS TOO?

ABSOLUTELY! THEIR LIVES REVOLVE ONLY ROUND THE VILLAGE GODDESS...THE INDOLENT LOT.

SO SHAYANPUR IS THE ONLY BLACK SPOT ON OUR KINGDOM, EH?

ANYONE WHO MAKES SHAYANPUR BUZZ WITH ACTIVITY WITHIN A YEAR, WILL WIN A FABULOUS REWARD.

53

55

SLEEP WELL TONIGHT AND BEGIN WORK EARLY TOMORROW.

HA! RICH! THAT'S WHAT I'M GOING TO BE...

AH! SO FAR SO GOOD! NOW FOR SOME SLEEP.

NEXT MORNING...

EAT WELL, TRAVELLER... YOU'VE BROUGHT ME GOOD FORTUNE.

NOT YET! YOU'LL BE RICH ONLY AFTER SIX MONTHS—THAT'S WHAT THE GODDESS SAID, REMEMBER?

OF COURSE, OF COURSE.

...AND DON'T FORGET TO START GROWING COTTON.

I'M OFF TO THE FIELDS RIGHT AFTER BREAKFAST.

BY THE WAY, WHAT WOULD YOU LIKE TO DO WHEN YOU GROW RICH?

UM... LET ME SEE... AH! GET MY DAUGHTER MARRIED, OF COURSE.

Panel 1:
THEN WHY DON'T YOU START PREPARING FOR IT RIGHT AWAY?

YES, WHY NOT? WIFE! RUN TO THE WEAVER AND ORDER THE BEST SARIS... I'M OFF TO THE FIELDS.

Panel 2:
SEE YOU IN THE EVENING, TRAVELLER.

...AND I'M OFF TO THE WEAVER'S HOUSE.

GOOD GOD! THEY'RE ON THEIR FEET FOR ONCE!

Panel 3:
AT THE WEAVER'S—

TEN SARIS FOR YOUR DAUGHTER'S WEDDING? WHO'S GOING TO PAY ME?

Panel 4:
MY HUSBAND! HE'S GOING TO BE RICH... YOU JUST WATCH.

WHO SAYS THAT?

Panel 5:
OUR GODDESS HERSELF SAID SO IN A DREAM.

OUR GODDESS, DID YOU SAY? I'LL GET TO WORK RIGHT AWAY!

Panel 6:
OH! OH! I MUST GET THE CARPENTER TO MEND THESE BEAMS.

Panel 7:
MEND YOUR LOOM? WHO DO YOU THINK IS GOING TO PAY ME?

WHEN THE WEAVER HAD RELATED THE WHOLE STORY —

OUR GODDESS, DID YOU SAY? I'LL MEND IT AT ONCE.

THESE TOOLS ARE ALL RUSTY. I MUST GET NEW ONES MADE.

AT THE BLACKSMITH'S —

NEW TOOLS? WHERE'S THE MONEY?

WELL IT'S LIKE THIS...

WHEN THE CARPENTER HAD FINISHED —

IF OUR GODDESS SAID SO, IT HAS TO BE TRUE!

AND THE BLACKSMITH SET TO WORK.

OH! I'LL NEED FIREWOOD TO LIGHT THE FURNACE...

AND SO, BY EVENING, THE WHOLE VILLAGE WAS BUSY AS A BEE-HIVE.

AT THE HEADMAN'S —

MY LOOM WILL BE READY IN A FEW WEEKS... I'LL THEN COME TO YOU FOR THE COTTON.

AH! I'VE PUT THEM BACK ON THE TRACK SOONER THAN I'D THOUGHT.

SURE, SURE! I'VE ALREADY STARTED GROWING IT.

59

Shikari Shambu

Script: Dev Nadkarni
Illustrations: V B Halbe

QUICK, PACK UP MY KIT. "SAFARI" MAGAZINE HAS ASSIGNED ME A NEW JOB.

WHAT KIND?

TO SHOOT TIGERS!

GOOD LORD! WHY WOULD THEY WANT YOU TO DO THAT?

OH! YOU'LL NEVER UNDERSTAND SUCH COMPLEX THINGS.

LATER—

LET'S FIND A GOOD SPOT AND BEGIN OUR JOB.

YES.

THIS PLACE SEEMS FINE...

WE'LL SETTLE DOWN HERE AND WAIT FOR A TIGER.

HUSH! SOMEONE'S COMING.

RUSTLE RUSTLE

OH! IT'S A BEAR.

SO WHAT? LET'S TRY IT OUT ON THIS BEAR FIRST... READY... AIM... SHOOT!

CLICK

*Did you know: Shambu's rifle is a tranquilizer used to put animals to sleep.

60

61

62

SETHJI'S NOSE Script & Illustrations: M. Yunus

IN A VILLAGE THERE LIVED A SETH AND HIS SETHANI.

SETHJI WAS FRIGHTENED OF THE DARK AND NEVER LEFT HIS HOUSE AT NIGHT...

...EXCEPT TO VISIT THE TOILET.

HE WOULD OPEN THE DOOR ...LOOK AROUND....

NO ONE...

NO THIEVES... NO DACOITS...

AFTERWARDS, HE WOULD QUICKLY RETURN TO HIS HOUSE.

ONE NIGHT HE WOKE UP...

...AND OPENED THE DOOR TO LOOK AROUND, WHEN —

SETHJI TRIED DESPERATELY TO PULL AWAY FROM THE THIEF.

THEN —

SETHANIJI, BRING ME FIVE HUNDRED RUPEES FROM MY SAFE, QUICKLY.

BUT WHY DO YOU WANT FIVE HUNDRED RUPEES AT THIS TIME OF THE NIGHT?

OH! BRING IT QUICKLY! THANK GOD THE THIEF IS ONLY HOLDING MY MOUSTACHE. IF HE CAUGHT MY NOSE, I WOULD HAVE TO GIVE HIM AT LEAST A THOUSAND RUPEES.

ONE THOUSAND FOR A NOSE...!

THE THIEF LEFT THE MOUSTACHE AND TRIED TO GRAB SETHJI'S NOSE, BUT...

...SETHJI QUICKLY PULLED BACK AND SHUT THE DOOR.

THE THIEF HAD TO GO AWAY, DISAPPOINTED.

THE FLUTE

Based on a story sent by K. Vijay Kiran

Illustrations: Goutam Sen

ONE DAY A POOR AND WEARY BEGGAR DECIDED TO REST UNDER A SPREADING TREE.

OH, I AM SO TIRED. I MUST HAVE WALKED MILES, BEGGING FOR ALMS TODAY. I THINK I WILL REST UNDER THIS SHADY TREE.

AHA! IT FEELS GOOD TO SIT DOWN. WHAT ON EARTH IS THAT NOISE?

TAP... TAP... TAP.

TAP... TAP... TAP...

OH, IT'S A WOODPECKER. MMM... THE TWIG IT IS PECKING AT SOUNDS HOLLOW.

OH DEAR, MY BEAK HAS GOT STUCK IN THIS HOLE — AND I HAD MADE THE OTHER SIX HOLES SO EASILY.

TRYING TO FREE HIS BEAK, THE BIRD STARTED TO BREATHE HEAVILY.

UH... UH... THE POOR THING SEEMS TO HAVE GOT HIS BEAK STUCK. I'LL FREE IT. BUT I WONDER WHERE THAT MUSICAL NOTE IS COMING FROM ... IT SEEMS TO BE FROM THE TWIG.

THERE YOU ARE... FLY AWAY, LITTLE BIRD. NOW LET ME EXAMINE THE TWIG AND SEE HOW IT WAS RESPONSIBLE FOR THAT SWEET SOUND.

HMM... IT'S A HOLLOW TWIG WITH SEVEN HOLES. WHEN THE WOODPECKER BREATHED HEAVILY THROUGH ONE HOLE, MUSICAL NOTES FLOWED OUT OF THE OTHERS.

THANK YOU, KIND MAN. YOU WILL SURELY BE AMPLY REWARDED.

SO THE BEGGAR PUT THE TWIG TO HIS LIPS AND BLEW THROUGH ONE OF THE HOLES.

WHAT WONDERFUL MUSIC THIS TWIG MAKES! I MUST SHOW THIS NEW INSTRUMENT TO THE KING HIMSELF.

WHERE ARE YOU GOING, MY GOOD MAN?

TO SEE THE KING! HAVE MADE A FANTASTIC DISCOVERY!

I WISH YOU ALL LUCK— AND IF YOU PLEASE THE KING'S DAUGHTER TOO, THEN YOUR FUTURE WILL HAVE BEEN MADE.

WHY DO YOU SAY THAT?

WELL, EVER SINCE THE QUEEN DIED, THE LITTLE PRINCESS HAS BEEN PINING AWAY. SHE NEITHER SMILES NOR TALKS AND HARDLY EATS ANYTHING. THE KING HAS PROMISED A REWARD TO ANYONE WHO CAN CHEER HER UP.

AT COURT THE NEXT DAY—

YOUR HIGHNESS, I BELIEVE I HAVE DISCOVERED A WONDERFUL NEW MUSICAL INSTRUMENT.

VERY WELL, PLAY IT FOR US.

AH... WHAT MUSIC!

VERY GOOD...! VERY GOOD INDEED!

FATHER..., WHAT IS THIS NEW INSTRUMENT? WHO IS THE MAN WHO PLAYS IT SO SKILFULLY?

DAUGHTER! AT LAST YOU ARE SHOWING AN INTEREST IN SOMETHING!

OH, FATHER, I AM ENTHRALLED! I'VE NEVER HEARD SUCH SOOTHING, RIPPLING MELODIES IN MY LIFE..., I FEEL SO MUCH HAPPIER ALREADY!

MY GOOD MAN, I AM OVERWHELMED. MY BELOVED DAUGHTER SMILES ONCE MORE. I GIVE YOU ALL THE RICHES YOU WANT AND HENCEFORTH DECLARE YOU TO BE THE COURT MUSICIAN.

YOUR HIGHNESS, YOU ARE VERY KIND!

IN COURSE OF TIME, THE TWIG WAS REPLACED BY A LENGTH OF BAMBOO AND THAT IS THE STORY OF THE FLUTE.

OH, MY FRIEND, DIDN'T I SAY YOUR KINDNESS TO A HELPLESS BIRD WOULD BRING YOU RICH REWARDS?

Again, Please!

Illustrations: Ram Waeerkar

Based on a story sent by
Kamal Borah

Readers' Choice

THE CLEVER CROW

Illustrations:
Goutam Sen

Based on a
story sent by
Prakash Babu

ONE DAY ALL THE BIRDS OF THE FOREST DECIDED TO CHOOSE A KING.

I CAN FLY HIGHER THAN ANY OF YOU, SO I SHOULD BE KING.

NO! I'M THE HANDSOMEST. I'M THE ONE WHO SHOULD BE MADE KING.

I CAN RUN FASTER THAN ANY OF YOU. I SHOULD BE CROWNED KING OF THE BIRDS.

I'M THE SWIFTEST FLIER. I SHOULD BE THE KING.

NO!

WHO'S THAT?

I CAN DO SOMETHING WHICH NONE OF YOU CAN. I CAN STOP A TRAIN.

HA HA HA! WHAT A HOPE!

THIS CROW'S A REAL OPTIMIST.

SO YOU DON'T BELIEVE ME, EH? I'LL SHOW YOU. COME ALONG.

HERE COMES A TRAIN. NOW WATCH.

69

70

THE PLAN THAT BACKFIRED!

A Nasruddin Hodja Tale

HODJA WAS VERY POPULAR AND ENTERTAINED OFTEN.

HODJA, I'VE COME TO YOUR HOUSE SO MANY TIMES THAT I'LL BE ABLE TO RECOGNIZE EVERY PIECE OF FURNITURE BLINDFOLDED.

BUT HODJA HAD ONE BITTER ENEMY—AHMED, THE WEAVER.

IT'S GOOD THAT HODJA'S GOING AWAY. I'LL PLAY A PRANK ON HIM. I'LL HAVE EVERY PIECE OF HIS FURNITURE CARTED AWAY, HEE HEE HEE!

UNFORTUNATELY FOR AHMED, HODJA RETURNED THAT SAME DAY—

TAKE THE FURNITURE TO MY HOUSE.

THAT'S AHMED... WHAT'S HE DOING? I'LL FOLLOW HIM AND FIND OUT.

THE CART IS GOING TOWARDS AHMED'S HOUSE.

MOVE EVERY PIECE INSIDE THE HOUSE.

YES, SIR.

SO THAT'S HIS GAME, BUT I'LL FIX HIM!

THE NEXT MORNING AHMED WENT OUT FOR A WALK. WHEN HE RETURNED—

HEY, HODJA! GET UP! WHAT ARE YOU DOING HERE?

SITTING ON THE PORCH OF MY NEW HOUSE, THAT'S WHAT!

72

QUESTIONS TO PLEASE

A Suppandi Tale

Illustrations:
Ram Waeerkar

Based on a story sent by Zia-ur-Rehman Siddiqui

SUPPANDI ONCE TOOK UP THE JOB OF A WAITER IN A RESTAURANT—

....AND REMEMBER, YOU MUST ALWAYS DO THINGS THAT MAKE THE CUSTOMER FEEL IMPORTANT.

ONE WAY TO DO THIS IS TO ASK RELEVANT QUESTIONS...

YES, YES, SIR!

AND SO—

WAITER! GET ME A CUP OF TEA.

HOT OR COLD?

ARE YOU JOKING? DOES ANYONE DRINK COLD TEA?! GET ME A CUP OF STEAMING, HOT TEA.

YES, SIR!

...ER...WOULD YOU LIKE TO HAVE IT IN A CUP OR A GLASS OR A...

OR A WHAT? WHAT ELSE CAN YOU SERVE TEA IN?

...A MUG?

NOW WILL YOU GET A CUP OF TEA OR...

YES, SIR, YES, SIR.

73

BUT...BUT... I ASKED HIM SO MANY QUESTIONS. HOW COME HE ISN'T PLEASED?

I KNOW WHAT—I DIDN'T ASK ENOUGH!

ER...SIR. YOU DIDN'T TELL ME HOW MUCH SUGAR...

THREE SPOONFULS!

ER... TEASPOONS OR TABLESPOONS?

YOU SILLY FOOL! ARE YOU OUT OF YOUR MIND?

I CANCEL MY ORDER FORTHWITH!

W... WHAT'S THE MATTER, SIR?

TELL ME, WHAT KIND OF RESTAURANT ARE YOU RUNNING? DO YOU SERVE FOOD OR JUST SERVE UP QUESTIONS?!

THE POOR MAN LEFT IN A HUFF...

...AND, NEEDLESS TO SAY, SUPPANDI SOON FOLLOWED SUIT.

DISGUISED FLATTERY

Based on a story sent by Don John Fernandes

READERS' CHOICE

Illustrations: Suresh Kshirsagar

THE PEOPLE OF A VILLAGE ONCE DECIDED TO BUILD A SCHOOL. EVERYONE CONTRIBUTED GENEROUSLY.

PLEASE DONATE GENEROUSLY, SIRS.

LATER—

EVERYONE'S CONTRIBUTED EXCEPT THE RICHEST MAN IN THE VILLAGE—RAMLAL.

THERE HE GOES.

WE MUST PERSUADE HIM. HE'S NEVER CONTRIBUTED TO ANYTHING SO FAR.

YOU ASK HIM. YOU ARE THE RIGHT MAN FOR THIS JOB.

ALL RIGHT.

AT RAMLAL'S —

SETHJI, WE ARE BUILDING A SCHOOL IN OUR VILLAGE. IT CANNOT BE BUILT WITHOUT YOUR ESTEEMED GUIDANCE AND BLESSINGS... AND OF COURSE, YOUR CONTRIBUTION.

WHY DO YOU APPROACH ME? DON'T YOU KNOW THAT I'M NEVER INFLUENCED BY FLATTERY?

YES, I KNOW THAT AND I'VE TOLD THE OTHERS...

...THAT THE GREAT SETH RAMLAL CAN NEVER BE WON OVER BY FLATTERY, HE IS INTELLIGENT ENOUGH TO DO WHATEVER HE THINKS IS BEST.

YOU'RE RIGHT... NOW HOW MUCH DO YOU NEED FOR THE BUILDING FUND?

Shikari Shambu

Script:
Dev Nadkarni

Illustrations:
V. B. Halbe

A FEW DAYS BEFORE THE VILLAGE FESTIVAL—

FOUR DAYS TO GO AND WE'VE NOT EVEN REHEARSED OUR ROLE FOR THE PLAY.

IT'S TOO CROWDED HERE... LET'S GO TO THE WOODS AND REHEARSE.

HAVE YOU PACKED UP THE COSTUMES?

I HAVE. LET'S HOPE NOBODY DISTURBS US IN THE WOODS.

THIS LOOKS LIKE A GOOD PLACE.

YES. LET'S BEGIN NOW.

MEANWHILE—

FE FI FO FUR... I SMELL THE SKIN OF A TIGER!

WHAAA!

?

A...A SHIKARI.

TH.... THIS TIGER T... TALKS!

*Did you know: Shambu's rifle is a tranquilizer used to put animals to sleep.

77

78

TANTRI
THE MANTRI

Script: Dev Nadkarni
Illustrations: Ashok Dongre

CLAP CLAP

WHY IS HE CLAPPING LIKE THAT?

OH, HE IS AN EXPERT MOSQUITO KILLER...

CLAP

EVERY TIME HE CLAPS, A DOZEN MOSQUITOES FALL DOWN.

SWAT

SEE?

HEH, HEH, I KNOW WHAT HE CAN DO FOR ME!

IF YOU GIVE ME THIS MONKEY, I'LL MAKE IT WORTH YOUR WHILE.

SURE, SURE. GO AHEAD — TAKE HIM AWAY.

HE'S REALLY QUICK!

79

BACK HOME —

NOW, TO PREPARE THIS SPECIAL PASTE, THE SMELL OF WHICH PUTS ONE TO SLEEP FOR WEEKS, WRAP IT UP IN A BALLOON...

... AND TIE IT ON THIS LITTLE FELLOW'S PALMS.

?

THAT DOES IT. I'LL NOW PRESENT HIM TO HOOJA AND WAIT TILL A MOSQUITO SETTLES ON HIS FACE...

AND WHEN THE MONKEY SLAPS HIS FACE TO KILL IT, THE BALLOON WILL BURST AND HOOJA'LL SMELL THE PASTE...

... AND FALL ASLEEP AT ONCE. THEN I'LL DECLARE MYSELF RAJA INSTEAD OF HOOJA.

SOON —

HE'S AN EXPERT MOSQUITO KILLER... HE'LL BE AN ASSET TO THE PALACE.

HE AMUSES ME, TANTRI !

81

A HELPING HAND

Illustrations : Ram Waeerkar

READERS' CHOICE

Based on a story sent by C. Venkatesh

Kalia
THE CROW

Script : **DENIS**
Illustrations :
RAM WAEERKAR

IT'S BEEN A LONG TIME SINCE WE MET OUR FRIEND THE RHINO.

YES! HIS LEG MUST BE CURED BY NOW. LET'S GO VISIT HIM.

I HOPE THEY DON'T RUN INTO ANY TROUBLE...

SUDDENLY...

OH NO!

HELLO, KEECHU, MEECHU.

DON'T HARM THE RABBITS, CHAMATAKA. YOU'LL BE SORRY.

HA, HA! SORRY, KALIA. IT'S JUST NOT YOUR DAY.

I MUST GET HELP... AND QUICKLY.

WAIT KALIA, DON'T LEAVE US!

83

84

85

MAKE A COTTON REEL TROT!

You will need: an empty cotton reel, a small rubber band, two matchsticks, adhesive tape, a piece of candle, scissors.

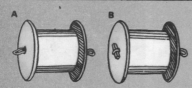

1. Using a matchstick, push the rubber band through the hole in the cotton reel so that it sticks out at both ends (A). Break a matchstick in two and slip half of it through one loop of the rubber band. Tape the matchstick and the rubber band to the reel (B).

2. Cut off about 1 cm. of the candle and poke out the wick with the scissors leaving a hole through the centre. Push the free loop of the rubber band through the candle (C). Take a whole matchstick and place it firmly through this loop (D). Wind up the matchstick by twisting it. Then place the reel on a smooth surface. It will click-clack along like a small robot

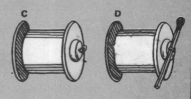

3. When you wind up the matchstick, you store up energy in the rubber band. The more you coil the band, the greater the energy it will release on unwinding, and the further the cotton reel will run.

MADE FOR EACH OTHER

Illustrations: Ram Waeerkar

Story sent by
Vidya Ramamoorthy

Readers'
Choice

IF YOU LEAVE BEFORE DAWN TOMORROW, YOU'LL REACH MAN'S HOUSE IN TIME FOR BREAKFAST.

AND DON'T FEEL SHY AT LUNCH TIME. HAVE YOUR FILL, AND SKIP DINNER AT HOME.

THAT'S WHAT I INTEND DOING!

THEREFORE, EARLY NEXT MORNING—

SUDDENLY—

DID I... OR DIDN'T I?

YOU ARE BACK? SO SOON?

DID I LEAVE THE LAMP BURNING? HAVE YOU PUT IT OF?

OF COURSE, I PUT IT OFF!

YOU'VE WORN OUT YOUR GOOD, COSTLY SHOES IN COMING BACK!

DO YOU THINK I'M A FOOL?

I TOOK THEM OFF AND CARRIED THEM IN MY HAND!

KRISHNA'S COW

Illustrations:Dilip Kadam

Based on a story sent by Paramjeet Singh

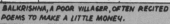

BALKRISHNA, A POOR VILLAGER, OFTEN RECITED POEMS TO MAKE A LITTLE MONEY.

WAH! WAH!

EXCELLENT, BALKRISHNA! YOU DESERVE AN AWARD. SEE ME TOMORROW.

HUH! THAT'S WHAT HE ALWAYS SAYS. HE HAS NEVER GIVEN ME A COWRIE. HIS 'TOMORROWS' NEVER COME.

SOON IT WAS THE ZAMINDAR'S DAUGHTER'S WEDDING AND BALKRISHNA WAS ASKED TO RECITE POEMS.

I MUST OUTWIT THE ZAMINDAR TODAY.

CLAP! CLAP!

WELL DONE, BALKRISHNA! TOMORROW I WILL REWARD YOU AMPLY.

WHY TOMORROW, SIR?

TODAY IS AN AUSPICIOUS DAY AND THERE ARE SUCH ESTEEMED GUESTS HERE TOO.

YES, HE IS RIGHT.

THE ZAMINDAR CALLED A SERVANT AND—

AFTER A WHILE THE SERVANT RETURNED WITH A COW.

BALKRISHNA THEN WENT NEAR THE COW, AND—

90

I AM SORRY, MOTHER! DO FORGIVE ME!

?

WHAT'S ALL THIS, BALKRISHNA?

WELL, SIR...

...I ASKED THE COW A SIMPLE QUESTION.

QUESTION? WHAT QUESTION?

I JUST ASKED HER IF SHE'D BE ABLE TO GIVE ME CALVES. AND SHE GOT VERY ANGRY.

WHY?

SHE SAID, "CAN'T YOU SEE I BELONGED TO KRISHNA'S HERD! I HAVE SEEN THE GREAT MAHABHARATA WAR...

"... AND THE ERA OF BUDDHA AND MAHAVIRA TOO...

"... AND YOU, INSOLENT BOY, ASK ME SUCH AN INSULTING QUESTION!"

HE HAS A POINT THERE.

HA! HA!

BALKRISHNA'S TRICK WORKED. THE ZAMINDAR QUICKLY REPLACED THE OLD COW WITH A YOUNGER, HEALTHIER ONE.

THE LOTUS
Our National Flower
Script :
Prof (Mrs) S.M. Almeida

Illustrations :
J.P. Irani

THE LOTUS GROWS IN SWEET, SHALLOW AND STAGNANT WATER.

THE FLOWERS ARE SCENTED. THEY OPEN AT SUNRISE AND CLOSE IN THE AFTERNOON.

THEY STAND ERECT ON LONG STALKS ABOVE THE WATER LEVEL.

THE LEAVES ARE LARGE, DARK GREEN AND SHINY.
THEIR UPPER SURFACE HAS A WAXY COATING.
WATER DROPS FALLING ON THE LEAVES RUN OFF LIKE SILVERY WHITE GLOBULES.
STRONG VEINS ON THEIR LOWER SURFACE HELP THEM TO STAND IN POSITION AND WITHSTAND WATER CURRENTS.

VEINS

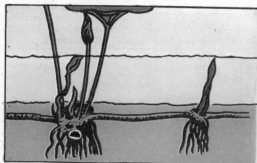

THE STEM OF THE LOTUS LIES BURIED IN THE MUD OF THE LAKE OR POND. IT IS A CREEPING STEM AND IT LIES HORIZONTALLY UNDER THE MUD. SPONGY ROOTS GROW OUT FROM IT. THE ROOTS FIX THE PLANT FIRMLY IN THE SOIL AND ALSO SUCK UP NOURISHMENT FROM IT.

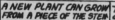

A NEW PLANT CAN GROW FROM A PIECE OF THE STEM

THE STEM ITSELF IS SWOLLEN WITH FOOD MATERIAL. THE FOOD MATERIAL IS STORED IN THE FORM OF STARCH.

THE STEM IS USED AS A VEGETABLE. IT HAS MEDICINAL USES TOO.

THE FRUIT OF THE LOTUS TOO, CAN BE EATEN

THE LOTUS SEED HAS A THIN BUT HARD SHELL. THE ALMOND—COLOURED KERNEL IS NUTRITIOUS. THE GREEN DORMANT BUD IS BITTER AND MUST BE REMOVED BEFORE EATING.

THE WATER LILY

UNLIKE THE LEAVES OF THE LOTUS WHICH STAND ABOVE THE SURFACE OF THE WATER, THE LEAVES OF THE WATER LILY FLOAT ON THE WATER.

THE ANTELOPE IS HEAVIER THAN HER, BUT THAT PRESENTS NO PROBLEM TO THE LEOPARDESS.

THERE! SHE HAS REACHED THE TOP HERE THE PREY IS SAFE FROM THE REACH OF HYENAS AND JACKALS.

SOMETIMES LEOPARDS LIE IN WAIT ON THE BRANCH OF A TREE ...

... AND LEAP DOWN ON PREY PASSING BENEATH.

BEING SOLITARY ANIMALS, INTRUSION OF ONE LEOPARD INTO ANOTHER'S TERRITORY MAY RESULT IN A FIGHT. IF THEY ARE EVENLY MATCHED THEN THEY MAY SEPARATE AND GO THEIR WAYS. BUT USUALLY IT IS A FIGHT TO THE FINISH.

AS MAN ENCROACHES UPON FORESTS, THE HABITAT OF THE LEOPARD, ITS NATURAL PREY, THE HERBIVOROUS ANIMALS ARE FORCED TO MIGRATE. THE LEOPARD THEN PREYS UPON DOMESTICATED ANIMALS LIKE GOATS AND CATTLE.

SOME LEOPARDS, ESPECIALLY THOSE FOUND IN ASIA, HAVE BIGGER AND DARKER SPOTS. SUCH LEOPARDS ARE CALLED PANTHERS. THE TERM 'PANTHER' IS ONLY USED AS A GENERAL CLASSIFICATION. EVEN PUMAS ARE KNOWN AS PANTHERS.

PANTHER

LEOPARDS ARE OFTEN CONFUSED WITH CHEETAHS. CHEETAHS BELONG TO A DIFFERENT SPECIES ALTOGETHER (ACINONYX JUBATUS). THEY ARE SMALLER IN SIZE THAN LEOPARDS.

CHEETAH

HOT TREATMENT

A Suppandi Tale

Readers' Choice

Based on a story sent by: S. Raamganesh

Illustrations: Sanjiv Waeerkar

BLUB... SUPPANDI, I HAVE TO ATTEND AN IMPORTANT MEETING SO PLEASE PRESS MY SUIT.

CERTAINLY, SIR.

SUPPANDI, WHAT ARE YOU DOING?

PRESSING YOUR SUIT, SIR.

OH, YOU FOOL! YOU MUST PRESS IT WITH A HOT IRON.

OH, I SEE.

ALWAYS USE THE HOT IRON AND YOUR BRAINS.

I WILL REMEMBER THAT.

DID YOU KNOW?

Before stamps came into use, it was costly to receive a letter. More often than not, the postage had to be paid by the receiver. Many people sent their message in code written on the outside of the letter so that the receiver did not have to open it and therefore, did not have to pay for it.

Penny Black

The first postage stamp of the world, the 'Penny Black' was issued in Great Britain on 6th May, 1840.

The first postage stamps for general use all over India were issued on July 1, 1854. The stamps were in denominations of half an anna, one anna, two annas and four annas and portrayed Queen Victoria of England.

Indian stamp of 1854

Till 1926, Indian stamps were printed in London. Then it became the responsibility of the India Security Press, Nasik.

Shoes for HODJA

A Nasruddin Hodja Tale

Script: Dev Nadkarni
Illustrations: Ram Waeerkar

OF CABBAGES AND KINGS!

A Folktale from Karnataka

Script:
Nira Benegal

Illustrations:
V.B. Halbe

THE WITTIEST AND CLEVEREST MINISTER IN KING BHIMARAJ'S COURT WAS SUMATI. HIS FAME HAD SPREAD FAR AND WIDE...

I HAVE HEARD THAT KING BHIMARAJ'S MINISTER, SUMATI, IS VERY CLEVER.

...EVEN TO INDRAPUR, A RIVAL KINGDOM, FAR UP NORTH.

YES, SIRE. PEOPLE SAY THAT WE'D BE HARD-PRESSED TO FIND ANYONE MORE CLEVER.

HA! I REFUSE TO BELIEVE THAT! WE'LL TEST HIM... NOW LISTEN. HERE'S WHAT WE'LL DO...

MANY WEEKS LATER AT MANGALAPURA, KING BHIMARAJ'S KINGDOM—

YOUR MAJESTY, I BRING YOU GREETINGS FROM KING JAYARAJ OF INDRAPUR!

THANK YOU WHAT CAN WE DO FOR HIM?

HE'S HEARD OF THE SUCCULENT CABBAGES AND RADISHES YOU HAVE HERE IN MANGALAPURA...

THAT'S TRUE— OUR VEGETABLES ARE RATHER GOOD!

KING JAYARAJ WOULD LIKE VERY MUCH TO TASTE SOME!

HMM... WE'LL SEE WHAT WE CAN DO.

101

LATER, KING BHIMARAJ CALLED SUMATI TO HIS PRIVATE CHAMBERS.

SUMATI, WE'RE IN TROUBLE. I CAN'T ALLOW JAYARAJ TO GET THE BETTER OF ME

NO, YOU CAN'T, YOUR MAJESTY.

BUT HE WILL—HE WANTS TO EAT SOME OF OUR CABBAGES AND RADISHES!

OH!

HOW CAN WE SEND THEM TO HIM WHEN IT TAKES THREE MONTHS TO REACH INDRAPUR?

THEY'LL ROT BY THE TIME THEY REACH!

I AGREE IT'S A PROBLEM, SIRE. BUT NOT IMPOSSIBLE.

WELL, YOU BETTER THINK OF SOMETHING, SUMATI ... AND QUICKLY.

THE NEXT DAY—

THERE'S A WAY OUT, SIRE. BUT I WILL NEED TWO CARTS, FOUR BULLOCKS AND FOUR TRUSTED MEN.

YOU'LL HAVE THEM, SUMATI.

SO SUMATI GOT BUSY—

FILL THESE CARTS WITH RICH SOIL MIXED WITH MANURE...

NOW BRING THE BEST QUALITY CABBAGE AND RADISH SEEDS.

102

103

WHERE ARE THEY?

WOULD YOU BE SO GOOD AS TO STEP OUTSIDE, YOUR MAJESTY!

HERE THEY ARE, YOUR MAJESTY!

KING BHIMARAJ AND MINISTER SUMATI WISH YOU "HAPPY EATING", YOUR MAJESTY!

MY GOD, THE VEGETABLES ARE GROWING IN THESE CARTS AND ARE NOW READY TO BE EATEN!

I'M SURE I'LL ENJOY THEM. THANK YOUR KING AND HIS MINISTER FOR THEIR KIND GIFTS

BUT YOU MUST NOT GO AWAY EMPTY-HANDED. I'LL FILL THESE CARTS WITH SOME GIFTS FOR THE PEOPLE OF MANGALAPURA

THANK YOU, YOUR MAJESTY!

LATER—

I CONCEDE DEFEAT! THAT SUMATI IS REALLY VERY CLEVER!

Kalia
THE CROW

Script
and
Illustrations
PRASAD IYER B.

WE MUST FIND THE LEOPARD THAT HAS ESCAPED

YES. THE REWARD THE ZOO'S OFFERING IS WORTH ANY EFFORT.

SO A LEOPARD IS ON THE PROWL. I'D BETTER GO AND SEE IF MY FRIENDS ARE SAFE.

MEANWHILE —

A RABBIT!

GOT YOU!

LET ME GO! LET ME GO!

OH NO, HE'S CAUGHT MEECHU.

LET GO OF THAT RABBIT.

NOT A CHANCE.

105

106

107

You Can't Treat Me! Based on an idea sent by Brat Kumar Sharma

See and Smile

Savio Mascarenhas

108

The Adventures of SUPPANDI

"THE EXPANDING CHAPPALS"

Illustrations :
Ram Waeerkar

based on a story sent by
P. Bharathi

READERS' CHOICE

110

CHATTU'S UMBRELLA

Illustrations: Dilip Kadam

Readers' Choice
Based on a story sent by
M. Pradyu

CHATTU, A FOOLISH MAN, WENT TO THE MARKET WITH HIS BAG AND UMBRELLA.

AFTER HE HAD DONE HIS SHOPPING AND WAS GOING HOME—

HEY! WHERE'S MY UMBRELLA?

I MUST'VE LEFT IT IN ONE OF THE SHOPS.

IS MY UMBRELLA HERE?

NO.

IS MY UMBRELLA HERE?

NO.

FINALLY HE WENT TO THE VERY FIRST PLACE HE HAD SHOPPED AT—

IS MY UMBRELLA HERE?

YES.

YOU'RE THE ONLY HONEST SHOPKEEPER HERE.

ALL THE OTHERS DENIED HAVING MY UMBRELLA.

!

Shikari Shambu

Script:
Denis

Illustrations:
V.B. Halbe

AH! WHAT A GLORIOUS DAY FOR HUNTING.

SAHEB, TEA!

NOT NOW — I WANT TO GO OUT INTO THE GARDEN.

LAZY FELLOW... HE PROMISED TO CUT THE GRASS LAST WEEK, BUT...

AH, HUNTING! WHAT A LIFE! I CAN SEE THE TIGER. THERE HE IS... BANG!

OH! THERE'S ANOTHER ONE UP THERE. BANG...

SUDDENLY —

GET UP!

HEH!

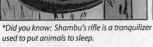

*Did you know: Shambu's rifle is a tranquilizer used to put animals to sleep.

INSTEAD OF DAY-DREAMING WHY DON'T YOU CUT THE GRASS?

I WASN'T DAY-DREAMING. I WAS MAKING PLANS FOR THE NEXT HUNT.

YOU'VE GOT TO HELP US, SAHEB.

A LEOPARD RAIDED THE HEN-COOP TODAY.

YESTERDAY, HE TOOK OFF WITH A LAMB.

I'LL TAKE CARE OF THE LEOPARD...

FIRST YOU WILL CUT THAT GRASS OR ELSE...

OF COURSE! HEE, HEE, HEE.

HAVE SOME PATIENCE AND I'LL GET THAT LEOPARD...

CUTTING GRASS IS SO EASY. I HAVE CUT DOWN TIGERS, LIONS AND...

SNIP... SNIP...

UH... LEOPARD!

114

GENEROUS CONTRIBUTION

Based on a story sent by Deepak Saha

Illustrations: Ram Waeerkar

THE WISHING WELL Illustrations: Teegies

Readers' Choice
Based on a story sent by
D. Saravana Kumar

PASHA, THE COOK, RETURNED HOME AFTER WORKING AT A GRAND WEDDING.

WIFE! WIFE! LOOK, WHAT I'VE BROUGHT!

WHAT? WHERE?

HERE! RIGHT BEHIND ME!

BUT THAT'S BHOORI— OUR GOAT. WHAT HAVE YOU BROUGHT FROM THE WEDDING?

I'VE BROUGHT A CARTLOAD OF TREASURE!

YOU SILLY WOMAN! CAN'T YOU SEE?

HERE! HERE!

... BUT, OF COURSE, YOU CAN'T!

WHAT DO YOU MEAN? I'M NOT BLIND.

NO, YOU'RE NOT! BUT, LET ME EXPLAIN. WHILE RETURNING I WAS PASSING THROUGH A FOREST...

"WHEN I CAME UPON A WELL, I WENT NEAR IT FOR A DRINK OF WATER.

SUDDENLY —

WHO IS THERE?

IT'S I... PASHA, SIR. WHO ARE YOU?

I'M THE GHOST WHO GUARDS THIS WISHING WELL. DO YOU WANT SOMETHING, PASHA? THROW A GOLD COIN IN IF YOU DO.

A...GOLD... COIN...?

WELL... THINK IT OVER! YOU CAN GET THOUSANDS OF COINS!

ALL RIGHT! HERE YOU ARE...

...PLEASE GIVE ME A CARTLOAD OF JEWELS AND COINS, SIR!

"AND THEN OUT CAME BUNDLES OF COINS AND JEWELS."

I STARTED ON MY JOURNEY, WHEN A THOUGHT STRUCK ME.

WHAT?

THE FEAR OF ROBBERS IN THAT THICK JUNGLE MADE ME GO BACK TO THE WELL...

...WHERE I THREW THE SECOND COIN I HAD EARNED, AND WISHED —

O GHOST! PLEASE MAKE MY TREASURE INVISIBLE TO EVERYONE BUT ME.

IT WILL BE SO, PASHA.

INK!

OH YOU SILLY MAN! HOW WILL YOU USE THE MONEY AND GOLD WHICH NO ONE CAN SEE?

AND YOU HAVE LOST YOUR GOOD GOLD COINS TOO... BOO...HOO...SOB...SOB...!

DON'T CRY! DON'T CRY! I'M SURE THE GHOST WILL HELP.

PASHA HURRIED BACK TO THE WELL AND —

HERE!

TAKE IT! TAKE IT ALL BACK! BUT PLEASE RETURN MY COINS!

WELL, MY DEAR PASHA...

...I'M SORRY, IT CAN'T BE DONE! YOU'VE ALREADY BEEN GIVEN TWO WISHES IN EXCHANGE FOR THOSE TWO GOLD COINS!

PASHA BEGGED AND PLEADED, BUT ALL WAS IN VAIN.

118

ANWAR

by
Appaswami

Illustrations: V. B. Halbe

119

NEEDLESS HONESTY

Based on a story sent by A. Mohan

Illustrations :
Suresh Kshirsagar

READERS' CHOICE

* TICKET-COLLECTOR

120

YOU...YOU...MADMAN. YOU'VE STOPPED THE TRAIN.

I TOLD YOU, I WANTED THE T.C.

SOON THE GUARD ENTERED —

NOW THEN, WHO PULLED THE CHAIN! COME ON, SPEAK UP!

I DID. I WANTED THE T.C.

WHAT FOR?

THIS IS MY DAUGHTER. SHE TURNED THIRTEEN AT MIDNIGHT. SINCE SHE WAS TWELVE-YEARS OLD YESTERDAY, I BOUGHT ONLY A HALF-TICKET FOR HER...

NOW I WANT TO EXCHANGE IT FOR A FULL-TICKET. THAT'S WHY I WANTED THE T.C.

?!

HA HA HA! OH MY, I'VE NEVER HEARD OF ANYTHING LIKE THIS BEFORE.

WELL, THE T.C. WILL BE ALONG SOON. BUT YOU HAVE TO PAY Rs. 250 FOR PULLING THE CHAIN.

COME ON! PAY UP!

SO POOR BOLAI BABU HAD TO PAY UP.

121

Readers' Choice

EGGS FOR THE KING

Based on a story sent by
V. Srikant

Illustrations:
Ram Waeerkar

GULABRAO AND HIS WIFE JANAKI OWNED AN INN IN THE SMALL VILLAGE OF JAIGAD. ONE DAY...

OOOOH... OOOOH! HUSBAND, DEAR, COME QUICKLY AND SEE WHO HAS COME TO OUR HUMBLE INN.

WHY... WHY IT'S THE KING HIMSELF. HO! HO! HO! THIS IS OUR LUCKY DAY!

INDEED! I WILL COOK A SPLENDID FEAST. I'LL MAKE PULAO... I'LL MAKE BASUNDI.*

WE'LL BE RICH!

WE'LL BE RICH!

GULABRAO AND JANAKI RUSHED OUT TO GREET THE KING.

YOUR HIGHNESS.

YOUR HIGHNESS, WELCOME TO OUR HUMBLE ABODE.

TELL US, YOUR HIGHNESS. WHAT CAN WE DO FOR YOU?

YOUR WISH IS OUR COMMAND.

AH! DEAR INNKEEPER, I'M TIRED AND WEARY. WHAT I WOULD RELISH MOST OF ALL IS A PLATE OF SCRAMBLED EGGS.

SCRAMBLED EGGS!

SCRAMBLED EGGS?

SCRAMBLED EGGS!

* A KIND OF PORRIDGE

122

Did you know?

Text: Swarn Khandpur
Illustrations: Goutam Sen

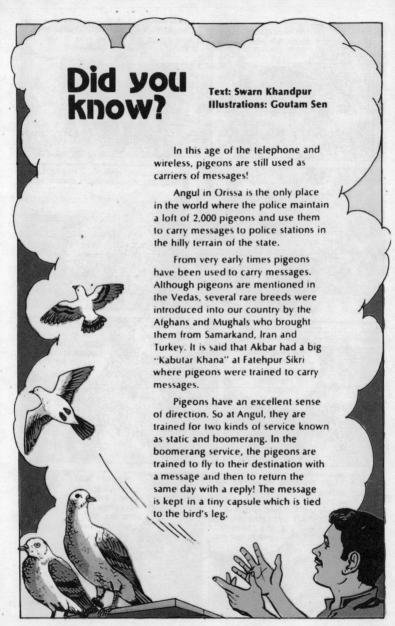

In this age of the telephone and wireless, pigeons are still used as carriers of messages!

Angul in Orissa is the only place in the world where the police maintain a loft of 2,000 pigeons and use them to carry messages to police stations in the hilly terrain of the state.

From very early times pigeons have been used to carry messages. Although pigeons are mentioned in the Vedas, several rare breeds were introduced into our country by the Afghans and Mughals who brought them from Samarkand, Iran and Turkey. It is said that Akbar had a big "Kabutar Khana" at Fatehpur Sikri where pigeons were trained to carry messages.

Pigeons have an excellent sense of direction. So at Angul, they are trained for two kinds of service known as static and boomerang. In the boomerang service, the pigeons are trained to fly to their destination with a message and then to return the same day with a reply! The message is kept in a tiny capsule which is tied to the bird's leg.

124

BUY? BYE!

A Nasruddin Hodja tale

Based on a story sent by Katyayani Juloori

Illustrations: Ram Waeerkar

ONE DAY HODJA SET OUT TO BUY A LAMP.

THERE GOES HODJA. I'LL FOLLOW HIM AND HAVE SOME FUN!

HOW MUCH IS THAT LAMP?

THIRTY RUPEES!

THIRTY? I'LL TAKE IT.

NO, NO, I'D LIKE TO BUY THAT LAMP. I'LL PAY YOU MORE!

BUT I ASKED FOR IT FIRST!

HUSH, HODJA! HOW MUCH WILL YOU PAY?

FIFTY RUPEES!

FIFTY! BUT... BUT HODJA WAS HERE FIRST!

I'LL...I'LL PAY YOU SEVENTY-FIVE!

HODJA?

GIVE IT TO HIM.

IT'S YOURS FOR SEVENTY-FIVE!

?!

I'M OFF TO THE NEXT SHOP— THERE'S ONE THERE JUST LIKE IT FOR ONLY THIRTY.

?!

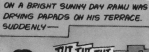

TURNING THE (VEGE) TABLES

A Nasruddin Hodja tale

Illustrations:
Ram Waeerkar

Based on a story sent by
Rajendra Pillai

(Readers' Choice)

NASRUDDIN HODJA WAS ACCOMPANYING THE SULTAN ON AN INSPECTION TOUR OF THE KINGDOM. THEY PASSED A FIELD OF CABBAGES.

AH! JUST LOOK AT THOSE CABBAGES... THEY LOOK SO JUICY!

YES, YOUR MAJESTY. THE CABBAGE IS INDEED THE BEST OF ALL VEGETABLES.

BUT, NOW THAT YOU MENTION IT, I AM NOT PARTICULARLY FOND OF EATING CABBAGES. I ONLY LIKE THEIR APPEARANCE.

BUT, OF COURSE! THE CABBAGE IS THE WORST OF ALL VEGETABLES.

NASRUDDIN, HOW CAN YOU CHANGE YOUR MIND SO QUICKLY?

IT'S SIMPLE, YOUR MAJESTY. I AM YOUR SERVANT, NOT THE SERVANT OF CABBAGES!

OIL PAINT PATTERNS

You will need some oil-based paints, a big bowl, water and a sheet of drawing paper.

1. Fill the bowl with water

2. Now pour a little of the oil paints (different colours) onto the water. Stir gently.

3. Hold the sheet of paper by the corners.

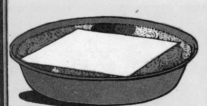

4. Lay it on the surface of the water. Then lift it up carefully and allow it to dry.

You will find that a complex pattern has formed on the paper.

THE MAGIC OF WRITING

Illustrations: Anand Mande

THE LANDLORD OF SIMAPUR HAD A HARD-WORKING, BUT ILLITERATE, SERVANT. ONE DAY—

GO AND GIVE THESE MANGOES TO MY DAUGHTER IN THE NEXT VILLAGE ALONG WITH THIS LETTER.

IS THERE ANY MESSAGE FOR HER, SIR?

NO. THE LETTER WILL TELL HER EVERYTHING.

ON THE WAY—

I'M HUNGRY. I'LL EAT SOME MANGOES...BUT... OH, OH...THE LETTER...

...THE LETTER WILL TELL THE MASTER'S DAUGHTER THAT I ATE SOME MANGOES...

...SO I'LL BURY IT UNDER THIS EARTH. THEN IT WON'T BE ABLE TO SEE ME EATING!

CHOMP SLURP

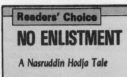

Readers' Choice

NO ENLISTMENT

A Nasruddin Hodja Tale

Based on a story sent by
T.R. Ganesh

Illustrations : Ram Waeerkar

ONE DAY HODJA AND HIS NEPHEW WERE RETURNING HOME FROM A FAIR.

DID YOU ENJOY YOURSELF?

OH, YES, UNCLE. VERY MUCH.

SOON THEY WERE PASSING THROUGH AN ARMY CAMP.

HOLD ON TIGHTLY TO MY HAND.

HA HA HA! LOOK AT THAT BABY-SITTER HOLDING ON TO HIS BABY.

AND A GROWN-UP BABY AT THAT! HO HO HO!

HEY, YOU! WHY ARE YOU HOLDING ON SO TIGHTLY TO THAT BOY?

THINK HE'LL GET LOST?

SUCH IMPUDENCE.

IT'S BECAUSE I DON'T WANT HIM TO DO SOMETHING STUPID...

... LIKE RUNNING AWAY TO JOIN THE ARMY!

EH?

P?!

THE KING OF MITHAPUR WAS VERY STERN INDEED. ONE DAY—

I WANT YOU ALL TO KNOW THAT ALL THE PEOPLE IN MY KINGDOM ARE MY SERVANTS.

NO, YOU'RE QUITE MISTAKEN, YOUR MAJESTY. ALL MEN ARE SERVANTS OF ONE ANOTHER, NOT OF ONE MAN.

WHAT!

DOES THAT MEAN THAT I AM YOUR SERVANT?

YES, YOUR MAJESTY, AND I CAN PROVE IT.

VERY WELL, YOU HAVE UNTIL SUNDOWN TO PROVE IT. FAIL AND I'LL HAVE YOU PUNISHED.

YES, YOUR MAJESTY.

AT SUNDOWN—

THE KING WILL SOON BE COMING OUT. BE READY TO PLAY YOUR PART.

YES, SIR. YOU CAN RELY ON ME.

ALMS! ALMS!

HERE YOU ARE MY GOOD MAN. OOPS...

HELP ME, OR I'LL FALL!

DON'T WORRY, I'VE GOT YOU.

WELL, I WAS RIGHT, WASN'T I? YOU DID SERVE ME JUST NOW, DIDN'T YOU?

HA! HA! SO I DID!

THE KING, PLEASED WITH THE MINISTER'S CLEVERNESS, REWARDED HIM WELL.

An Idler's Aim

A Folk-tale from Rajasthan

Script: Nira Benegal
Illustrations: Goutam Sen

SO EVERY MORNING TEJA WOULD WAIT...

...UNTIL HIS NEIGHBOUR, THE STONE-CUTTER, HAD PASSED BY HIS HOUSE...

...AND THEN...

WIFE, NOW I CAN EAT!

BUT ONE DAY, TEJA'S NEIGHBOUR DID NOT APPEAR.

WHERE'S THAT STONE-CUTTER? I'VE BEEN WAITING FOR OVER AN HOUR...

...HE MUST HAVE LEFT EARLIER THAN USUAL TODAY. WHAT A BOTHER—I'LL HAVE TO GO TO THE QUARRY.

MEANWHILE, AT THE QUARRY—

THACK! THACK! CLUNK!

WHAT'S THIS?

IT'S A POT!

FULL OF GOLD!

AH! THERE YOU ARE!

THE GRAMOPHONE

Script :
Iyer Prasad B.

Illustrations :
Goutam Sen

THE FIRST-EVER MACHINE THAT COULD RECORD AND THEN REPRODUCE THE HUMAN VOICE WAS THE TIN-FOIL PHONOGRAPH, INVENTED BY THOMAS ALVA EDISON IN 1877. IT WAS POPULARLY KNOWN AS THE "TALKING MACHINE".

THE FIRST WORDS TO BE RECORDED AND PLAYED BACK WERE...

MARY HAD A LITTLE LAMB.

MARY HAD A LITTLE LAMB.

EDISON'S "TALKING MACHINE" WAS A SIMPLE MACHINE. IT HAD A TUBE FITTED AT ONE END WITH A VERY THIN DIAPHRAGM. A NEEDLE, CALLED STYLUS, WAS FIXED TO THE DIAPHRAGM. THE SHARP END OF THE NEEDLE PRESSED AGAINST TIN-FOIL WRAPPED ON A CYLINDER WHICH COULD BE ROTATED BY A HANDLE.

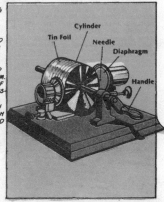

Cylinder

Tin Foil

Needle

Diaphragm

Handle

WHEN THE PERSON WHOSE VOICE WAS TO BE RECORDED SPOKE LOUDLY INTO THE TUBE, THE SOUND WAVES CAUSED THE DIAPHRAGM TO VIBRATE, MAKING THE STYLUS MOVE TO AND FRO.

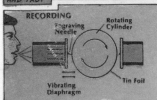

RECORDING

Engraving Needle

Rotating Cylinder

Vibrating Diaphragm

Tin Foil

AT THE SAME TIME THE CYLINDER WAS ROTATED AND THE STYLUS ENGRAVED A GROOVE OF VARYING DEPTH (DEPENDING ON THE TYPE OF SOUND MADE) ON THE TIN-FOIL.

TO REPRODUCE THE SOUND, THE ENTIRE PROCESS WAS REVERSED. A SIMILAR STYLUS-DIAPHRAGM-TUBE ARRANGEMENT (HEARING TUBE) WAS PRESSED AGAINST THE GROOVE ON THE 'RECORDED' CYLINDER. THE CYLINDER WAS THEN ROTATED. THE STYLUS MOVED TO AND FRO AS IT SLID ALONG THE GROOVE AND CAUSED THE DIAPHRAGM TO VIBRATE IN THE SAME WAY AS BEFORE.

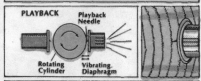

PLAYBACK

Playback Needle

Rotating Cylinder

Vibrating Diaphragm

THE VIBRATING DIAPHRAGM CAUSED VIBRATION IN THE AIR INSIDE THE TUBE AND THUS REPRODUCED THE ORIGINAL SOUND.

BUT WAS IT POSSIBLE TO GET A PERSONAL COPY OF THE RECORD? NO, NOT WITH EDISON'S MODEL! LATER MODELS, THE GRAMOPHONES, OPENED UP THE POSSIBILITY OF DUPLICATING THE RECORD. THE CYLINDER WAS REPLACED BY A TURN-TABLE ROTATED BY A CLOCKWORK MOTOR, AND THE GROOVED TINFOIL BY A GROOVED DISC.

Disc

Turntable

Motor

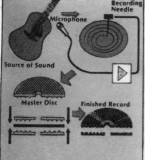

THE PRINCIPLE OF RECORDING REMAINED THE SAME AS THAT IN EDISON'S "TALKING MACHINE". BUT THE GROOVED DISC MADE IT POSSIBLE TO TAKE MOULDS TO MAKE A MASTER DISC. AND, FROM THE MASTER DISC, AS MANY COPIES AS WERE NEEDED COULD BE TAKEN.

Microphone

Recording Needle

Source of Sound

Master Disc   Finished Record

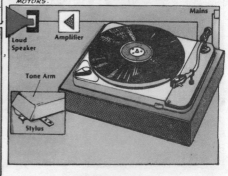

IN EARLIER GRAMOPHONES, THE TURN-TABLE WAS ROTATED BY A CLOCKWORK MOTOR, WOUND BY A HANDLE. IN MODERN GRAMOPHONES (CALLED RECORD PLAYERS) THEY ARE DRIVEN BY ELECTRIC MOTORS.

Mains

Loud Speaker   Amplifier

Tone Arm

Stylus

THE MODERN GRAMOPHONE SYSTEMS ARE A FAR CRY FROM THE EARLY ONES. THE DISCS ARE MADE BY A VERY COMPLICATED AND SOPHISTICATED PROCESS FOR BETTER REPRODUCTION. AND, WITH THE ADVENT OF ELECTRONICS, THE PLAYERS ARE MADE WITH FINE CONTROL OF TUNE AND TONAL QUALITIES.
BUT EDISON'S BASIC PRINCIPLE REMAINS.

Kalia
THE CROW

Script:
DEV NADKARNI
Illustrations:
IYER PRASAD B.

HELLO, SAYAL. IT'S AGES SINCE WE MET!

UH-HUH!

WHAT'S WRONG?

I SAW A TERRIBLE SIGHT, KALIA...

CHAMATAKA JUST PASSED THIS WAY CHASING TWO LITTLE KITTENS.

OH, DEAR.

QUICK, KALIA, THINK OF A WAY OF MAKING CHAMATAKA GIVE UP THE CHASE!

I AM.

AH!

HEY, HERE COMES DOOB DOOB.

LISTEN, SAYAL...

HELLO, KALIA.

HUH?

WHAT'S WRONG?

PLENTY. THAT NASTY VULTURE CLIPPED MY WINGS AND WHAT IS WORSE, I'VE HURT MY LEG TOO.

OH, OH.

IF YOU MEET BABLOO, SHONAR OR ANY OF MY FRIENDS, PLEASE TELL THEM I NEED HELP!

ER... SURE, KALIA. HEH...HEH. I MUST TELL CHAMATAKA... WHAT A CHANCE TO GET RID OF KALIA.

SOON —

CHAMATAKA, WAIT! HEY, CHAMATAKA!

WHAT DOES THAT FOOL WANT NOW?

CHAMATAKA! KALIA IS IN DEEP TROUBLE...

...AND HE CAN NEITHER FLY NOR WALK.

ARE YOU SURE THIS ISN'T ONE OF HIS TRICKS?

I AM. COME AND SEE FOR YOURSELF.

140

141

Readers' Choice

THE LIFE-LINE

Based on a story sent by
T.S. Kalyanasundaram

Illustrations:
Ram Waeerkar

RAM AND GOPAL WERE CROSSING A STREET WHEN—

VROOM! ZOOM!

WHEW!

ZOOM

THAT WAS A NARROW ESCAPE!

NO NEED TO WORRY...I BELIEVE IN PALMISTRY. SEE...

...MY LIFE LINE IS NICE AND LONG!

WELL, YOU AND I CAN SEE IT, BUT CAN TRUCK DRIVERS?

!

142

A LESSON FOR THE BARON

A Latvian Folktale

Script:
Prasad Iyer

Illustrations:
V.B. Halbe

ONE DAY A BARON SET OUT FOR A RIDE IN HIS CARRIAGE...

SUDDENLY—

CRRACK!

OOH! AAH! STOP.

THE WHEEL HAS COME OFF, SIR. I THINK IT'S BECAUSE OF A BROKEN NAIL.

WELL, GET IT REPAIRED THEN, YOU FOOL. THERE'S A VILLAGE OVER THERE.

AND SO THE CARRIAGE WAS TRUNDLED OVER TO THE VILLAGE BLACKSMITH'S.

I WANT THE WHEEL TO BE FIXED IMMEDIATELY.

HMM...THAT'S NO PROBLEM. ALL IT NEEDS IS A NAIL.

+ RUSSIAN MONEY   * A ROBBER OR BANDIT

THEN ONE DAY HE DROVE AWAY THE BLACKSMITH AND TOOK HIS PLACE.

WELL, COACHMAN, FROM TODAY YOU WILL BE MY ASSISTANT.

BUT... BUT I DON'T KNOW ANYTHING ABOUT THIS TRADE.

DON'T WORRY. JUST DO AS I TELL YOU.

AH! THERE'S OUR FIRST CUSTOMER.

SIR, I'M A FARMER AND I WANT THIS PIECE OF IRON TO BE MADE INTO A PLOUGHSHARE.

GIVE IT TO ME.

COACHMAN! LOOK SHARP THERE AND BLOW ON THE FIRE.

YES (PUFF PUFF), YES, SIR.

SOON THE IRON WAS RED-HOT AND THE BARON LAID IT ON THE ANVIL.

YOU THERE. START POUNDING THE IRON WITH THAT HAMMER.

YES, SIR.

THE FARMER STARTED HAMMERING THE PIECE OF IRON WITH A SLEDGE-HAMMER.

CLANG CLANG

AND THE BARON TOOK A SMALL HAMMER HIMSELF AND JOINED HIM IN BEATING THE METAL.

CLINK CLINK

THEY HAMMERED THE PIECE OF IRON FOR A LONG TIME AND IT BEGAN TO WEAR THIN—

WE'LL SPOIL THIS IRON PIECE IF WE KEEP ON HAMMER-ING.

FOOL! WHAT DO YOU KNOW ABOUT IT!

HERE, COACHMAN. YOU TAKE OVER FROM THIS LOUT!

AND SO—

BANG BANG
CLANG CLANG

I'VE NEVER SEEN SUCH POOR IRON AS YOURS. WE'LL NEVER BE ABLE TO MAKE IT INTO A PLOUGHSHARE. I'LL MAKE YOU AN AXE INSTEAD.

OH, ALL RIGHT. I CAN ALWAYS USE AN EXTRA AXE.

AND, SO THEY BEGAN HEATING THE IRON AND FORGING IT AGAIN. ALL THE TIME ITS SIZE KEPT ON SHRINKING AS MORE AND MORE OF THE METAL WAS LOST.

BANG BANG

OH, OH! I DON'T THINK THERE'S ENOUGH IRON HERE TO MAKE AN AXE. BUT TELL YOU WHAT... I'LL MAKE YOU A KNIFE.

OH... HUM... ALL RIGHT. GO AHEAD.

CLANG CLANG

SOON—

THIS IS VERY POOR IRON INDEED. NO KNIFE CAN BE MADE FROM THIS. I'LL MAKE YOU A NAIL INSTEAD.

ONLY A N...NAIL.

MAYBE YOU'D PREFER A TOOTHPICK.

OH, NO. I'LL TAKE THE NAIL.

A WISE DECISION, MY FRIEND.

AND SO THE PIECE OF IRON WAS HEATED, FORGED INTO A NAIL AND...

HISS

AH! JUST LOOK AT THAT! THE FINEST NAIL THAT EVER CAME OUT OF A BLACK-SMITH'S FORGE. TAKE IT, MY FRIEND.

NOW PAY ME TWO ROUBLES. AND THAT INCLUDES MY HELPER'S SHARE.

WHAT! THE CUNNING FELLOW —HE'S OUT TO SWINDLE ME. BUT I'LL FIX HIM.

I DON'T HAVE TWO ROUBLES. BUT I HAVE SOME FINE WHEAT AT HOME. I SHALL BE HAPPY TO LET YOU HAVE TWO ROUBLES' WORTH.

HMM... ALL RIGHT.

YOU GO AHEAD. WE'LL LOCK UP THE FORGE AND FOLLOW.

A LITTLE LATER THE BARON GOT INTO HIS CARRIAGE AND RODE TOWARDS THE FARMER'S HOUSE.

SOON HE ARRIVED.

NOW LOOK HERE. I'LL TAKE THIS SACK AND GO INTO THE STOREROOM. YOU STAY HERE AND KEEP YOUR EARS OPEN...

SOON THE FARMER WILL START FILLING THE SACK AND WHEN HE SAYS "THAT'S ENOUGH", YOU MUST SHOUT "NO. IT'S NOT. LET HIM HAVE MY SHARE TOO". UNDERSTAND?

YES, SIR.

INSIDE THE HOUSE THE FARMER AND HIS BRAWNY HELPERS WERE WAITING.

HERE HE COMES. GET READY.

GRAB HIM! LET HIM HAVE IT!

THWACK! THWACK! THWACK! THWACK!

148

THEY THRASHED THE BARON SOUNDLY. BUT HE BORE IT SILENTLY.

THAT'S ENOUGH!

THWACK!

THAT'S ENOUGH!

AH!

NO! IT'S NOT. GIVE HIM MY SHARE TOO!

YOU HEARD THAT! GIVE HIM SOME MORE!

YES, SIR.

THWACK THWACK!

FINALLY THE BARON TOTTERED OUT...

OOH! AAH! DRIVE HOME, COACHMAN.

...HAVING LEARNT A GOOD LESSON.

I DON'T WANT TO BE A BLACKSMITH EVER. IT'S TOO DANGEROUS!

Kalia
THE CROW

Script :
LUIS

Illustrations :
PRADEEP SATHE

GOOD NEWS, DOOB-DOOB!

HAVE YOU CAUGHT A DEER OR SOMETHING?

NO, NO! HOW CAN WE CATCH A DEER OR ANYTHING WHEN THAT PEST KALIA IS AROUND?

YOU'RE RIGHT.

I CAME TO TELL YOU THAT I KNOW WHERE HE LIVES.

WHERE?

ON THE TOP OF A TREE, NEAR BY.

OH, GOOD!

WE'LL HIDE IN HIS NEST AND WHEN HE COMES HOME... WHAM!

NEITHER OF US CAN CLIMB TREES, STUPID!

ER... THAT'S RIGHT.

SO HOW DO WE...

WE'LL BURN THE TREE DOWN!

150

151

153

CHANDRALEKHA

Adapted from a popular folktale from Tamil Nadu

Script: Rupa Gupta
Illustrations: M.N. Nangre

ONE EVENING CHANDRALEKHA, THE FAMOUS DANCER, LOST HER WAY IN THE WOODS.

IT'S GETTING DARKER.

MUCH LATER—

OH, WHAT AM I TO DO NOW?

SUDDENLY—

VOICES!

GOOD LORD! ROBBERS!

AH! THAT WAS A GOOD DAY'S WORK!

LET'S HIDE OUR LOOT HERE. BUT BEFORE WE DO...

...O MAGIC KANNAKOL* GO AND HIT ANY SPY WHO MAY BE AROUND.

THE KANNAKOL HIT HER BUT CHANDRALEKHA BRAVELY BORE THE PAIN WITHOUT A SOUND.

NO CRY! GOOD! THERE'S NO ONE AROUND. LET'S GET TO WORK.

HURRY UP. IT'S PAST MIDNIGHT.

THE TOWN MUST BE THAT WAY. I'LL TAKE THE TREASURE WITH ME.

* IT IS SAID THAT A KANNAKOL OBEYS ITS MASTER'S ORDERS.

155

THE NEXT DAY WHEN THE ROBBERS RETURNED TO THE SPOT—

OUR TREASURE IS GONE!

SOMEONE MUST HAVE SEEN US BURYING IT.

IMPOSSIBLE! THE KANNAKOL WOULDN'T MISS ANYONE. BUT I'LL EXAMINE IT ANY WAY.

BLOOD! SOME ONE WAS HIT!

WE WILL FIND THE CULPRIT.

LATER—

OINTMENTS... OINTMENTS FOR ALL WOUNDS...MIRACULOUS OINTMENTS...

HE MAY HAVE SOMETHING FOR MY WOUND! RUN! FETCH HIM.

ALL THIS MONEY IS YOURS IF YOU HAVE THE RIGHT OINTMENT FOR MY WOUND.

MY GOD! THAT WOUND IN HER ARM HAS BEEN MADE BY MY KANNAKOL.

OH OH! IT'S THE ROBBER CHIEF! I MUST BE ON MY GUARD.

LATER THAT NIGHT—

LOOK! LOOK! SHE HAS HIDDEN THE BOXES UNDER THE BED.

LET'S TEACH HER A LESSON. COME ON, PICK UP THE BED.

YOU THINK YOU'VE BEEN VERY CLEVER, MY FRIEND. BUT YOU ARE IN FOR A SURPRISE.

158

AY-EE-OH!

THE COWARD! RUNNING AWAY.

LET ME GO, CHIEF! I AM NOT AFRAID.

THE NEXT MINUTE—

A-AY-EE-OH!

SHE IS A DEVIL!

SHE HAS CUT OFF HIS NOSE!

RUN!

THEY'RE GONE, THANK GOD! AND I DON'T THINK THEY'LL DARE TO COME HERE AGAIN!

THE THOUSAND COINS — A Nasruddin Hodja tale

Script: Luis M. Fernandes
Illustrations: Ram Waeerkar

161

162

SOON —

YOUR HONOUR, LISTEN TO MY STORY! THIS MAN PRAYS LOUDLY EVERY MORNING...

THE NEIGHBOUR SPOKE FOR A LONG TIME. WHEN HE HAD FINISHED—

SO THE BAG OF MONEY WHICH THE HODJA FOUND IS YOURS!

THAT IS THE TRUTH, YOUR HONOUR.

DON'T BELIEVE HIM, YOUR HONOUR. HE IS ALWAYS CLAIMING OTHER PEOPLE'S PROPERTY AS HIS OWN.

I WON'T BE SURPRISED IF HE SAYS THAT THE MULE ON WHICH I RODE HERE IS HIS.

IT IS MINE!

NEXT, YOU'LL SAY THAT THIS COAT TOO IS YOURS!

IT IS! AND WELL YOU KNOW IT.

DO YOU SEE HOW IT IS, YOUR HONOUR?

I DO, INDEED!

163

164

MEET THE ANT

Based on the material provided by Nandini Deshmukh

Script: Ashvin
Illustrations: Pradeep Sathe

IT'S A WARM DAY AND THE RAINY SEASON WILL SOON BEGIN. YOU CAN SEE THE DRONES, THE MALE ANTS, THOUSANDS OF THEM, FROM HUNDREDS OF NESTS, UP IN THE AIR. THEY ARE WAITING FOR THEIR BRIDES. IT'S THE WEDDING SEASON FOR THEM.

AND HERE COME THE BRIDES. THEY ARE HEAVIER THAN THE DRONES.

AH! THIS DRONE HAS FOUND HIS MATE.

WHAT'S HAPPENED? THEY'RE FALLING DOWN—DOWN TO THE EARTH.

THE DRONE IS DEAD! AND THE BRIDE IS BREAKING HER WINGS. SHE IS A QUEEN NOW!

BUT WHERE IS HER FORTRESS? JUST WAIT AND SEE.

SHE IS GOING TO CRAWL UNDER THAT STONE AND DIG INTO THE EARTH.

HERE SHE IS, ALONE IN HER DARK LITTLE CHAMBER. SHE HAS SEALED THE ENTRANCE TO MAKE SURE SHE'S ABSOLUTELY SAFE. NOW IN THIS VERY PLACE, BY AND BY, SHE WILL RAISE A COLONY OF ANTS, THOUSANDS OF THEM.

AT LAST! HER FIRST BATCH OF EGGS HAVE APPEARED.

THEY ARE SOON FOLLOWED BY MANY MORE BATCHES. WHAT DOES SHE DO FOR FOOD MEANWHILE? SHE CAN'T GO OUT FOR FEAR OF HER ENEMIES. AND THERE IS NO FOOD IN HER CHAMBER.

NO FOOD? WHAT IS SHE EATING THEN? SOME OF HER OWN EGGS! SHE DOES IT BECAUSE SHE HAS TO LIVE TO RAISE A BIG FAMILY.

LOOK! SOME OF THE EGGS THAT SHE HASN'T EATEN HAVE BROKEN OPEN AND OUT HAVE COME THE LARVAE.

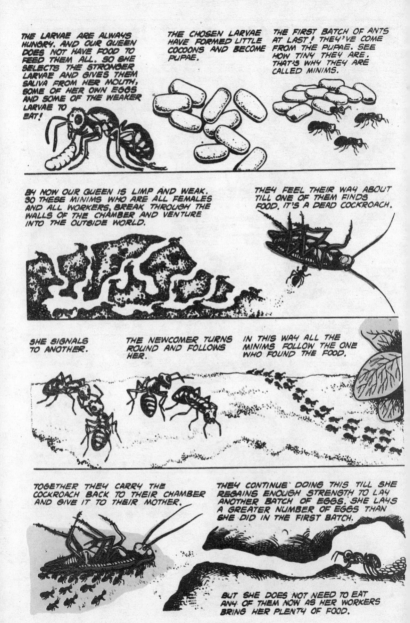

THE LARVAE ARE ALWAYS HUNGRY. AND OUR QUEEN DOES NOT HAVE FOOD TO FEED THEM ALL. SO SHE SELECTS THE STRONGER LARVAE AND GIVES THEM SALIVA FROM HER OWN MOUTH; SOME OF HER OWN EGGS AND SOME OF THE WEAKER LARVAE TO EAT!

THE CHOSEN LARVAE HAVE FORMED LITTLE COCOONS AND BECOME PUPAE.

THE FIRST BATCH OF ANTS AT LAST! THEY'VE COME FROM THE PUPAE. SEE HOW TINY THEY ARE. THAT'S WHY THEY ARE CALLED MINIMS.

BY NOW OUR QUEEN IS LIMP AND WEAK. SO THESE MINIMS WHO ARE ALL FEMALES AND ALL WORKERS, BREAK THROUGH THE WALLS OF THE CHAMBER AND VENTURE INTO THE OUTSIDE WORLD.

THEY FEEL THEIR WAY ABOUT TILL ONE OF THEM FINDS FOOD. IT'S A DEAD COCKROACH.

SHE SIGNALS TO ANOTHER.

THE NEWCOMER TURNS ROUND AND FOLLOWS HER.

IN THIS WAY ALL THE MINIMS FOLLOW THE ONE WHO FOUND THE FOOD.

TOGETHER THEY CARRY THE COCKROACH BACK TO THEIR CHAMBER AND GIVE IT TO THEIR MOTHER.

THEY CONTINUE DOING THIS TILL SHE REGAINS ENOUGH STRENGTH TO LAY ANOTHER BATCH OF EGGS. SHE LAYS A GREATER NUMBER OF EGGS THAN SHE DID IN THE FIRST BATCH.

BUT SHE DOES NOT NEED TO EAT ANY OF THEM NOW AS HER WORKERS BRING HER PLENTY OF FOOD.

THE ANTS THAT COME OUT OF THESE BATCHES ARE BIGGER AND STRONGER. THEIR ELDER SISTERS, THE WORKERS, HAVE KEPT THEM WELL FED TOO.

SOON THERE ARE HUNDREDS OF ANTS. BUT THE QUEEN CONTINUES TO LAY EGGS — MORE AND MORE OF THEM.

AND THE WORKERS HAVE PLENTY TO DO. BUT NOW THERE ARE MANY MANY MORE TO HELP. WHAT'S THIS THEY'RE DOING? IT'S A NEST. THEY'RE BUILDING A NEST.

LOOK AT THESE TUNNELS, PASSAGE-WAYS AND CHAMBERS. ALL BUILT BY THE WORKERS!

THEY HELP AT HOME TOO! AS SOON AS A BATCH OF EGGS BREAKS INTO LARVAE, THEY CARRY THEM TO THE SEPARATE CHAMBER RESERVED FOR LARVAE. AND WHEN THE LARVAE BECOME PUPAE, THEY TAKE THEM TO THE CHAMBERS RESERVED FOR PUPAE. AREN'T THEY HARD-WORKING!

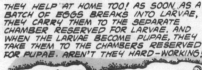

MANY OF THESE PUPAE TURN INTO SOLDIER ANTS. THESE SOLDIERS ARE ALL FEMALE ANTS. HERE ARE SOME OF THEM GUARDING THE ENTRANCE TO THE NEST BY BLOCKING IT WITH THEIR THICK SKULLS.

EVERY FEMALE ANT HAS A JOB TO DO. THEY NEVER IDLE.

BUT THE DRONES ARE LAZY FELLOWS. THEY TAKE NO PART IN THE WORK OF THE COLONY.

SOME OF THE EGGS OUR QUEEN LAYS TURN INTO A SPECIAL KIND OF FEMALES, THE WINGED-ONES. AND THESE ARE THE FUTURE QUEENS.

IT'S A WARM DAY. THE RAINY SEASON WILL SOON BEGIN. THE ANTS IN THE COLONY FEEL STRANGELY EXCITED. THE DRONES AND THE FUTURE QUEENS, THE WINGLESS SOLDIERS AND WORKERS ALL RUSH OUT INTO THE SUNSHINE.

AS THE DRONES AND THE WINGED FEMALES FLY AWAY IN SEARCH OF MATES FROM OTHER NESTS TO START THEIR OWN COLONIES, THE SOLDIERS AND WORKERS MAKE THEIR WAY BACK TO THEIR QUEEN AND THE COLONY THEY HAVE BUILT.

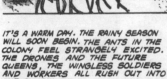

THE MAN WHO LOVED VADAS

Illustrations: M.N. Nangre

Based on a story sent by Srinivas Srivatsa

ONE DAY KHANDOBA, THE MISER, FELT LIKE EATING VADAS.

WIFE!

YES?

WILL YOU MAKE SOME VADAS FOR ME?

I WILL, IF YOU GET ME SOME OIL AND SOME DAL.

KHANDOBA PUT ON HIS TURBAN.

YOU'LL NEED THIS TIN FOR THE OIL, WON'T YOU?

NO, I WON'T.

KHANDOBA WENT TO A SHOP IN THE MARKET.

CAN YOU SHOW ME THE BEST OIL YOU HAVE?

TRY THIS ONE, SIR.

IT'S THE BEST IN THE MARKET.

LET ME SMELL IT AND SEE.

KHANDOBA BENT FORWARD, AS IF TO SMELL THE OIL.

THE NEXT MOMENT —

OH, DEAR! MY TURBAN!

OH, NO!

AS KHANDOBA PICKED UP THE OIL-SOAKED TURBAN —

I'M EXTREMELY SORRY, SIR. YOUR TURBAN...

NEVER MIND.

GIVE IT TO ME. I'LL HAVE IT WASHED AND ...

NO, MY FRIEND. I'M IN A HURRY.

I MUST LEAVE RIGHT AWAY. I'LL COME BACK LATER FOR THE OIL.

BACK AT HOME, KHANDOBA SQUEEZED THE OIL INTO A VESSEL.

THE VESSEL IS FULL.

BUT I DON'T UNDERSTAND WHY YOU BRING OIL IN YOUR TURBAN.

NOW TAKE THIS BAG.

WHAT FOR?

TO GET THE DAL.

I DON'T NEED YOUR BAG.

I HAVE MY TURBAN.

?

AT THE MARKET—

I WANT SOME GOOD DAL, SIR. CAN YOU SHOW ME THE BEST YOU HAVE?

HERE. HAVE A LOOK AT THE DAL IN THESE BAGS, SIR.

LET ME··· OH! MY TURBAN!

I'LL SEE YOU LATER.

AND KHANDOBA RETURNED HOME.

HERE YOU ARE! ALL THE DAL YOU NEED.

WHY COULDN'T YOU USE A BAG AS EVERYBODY ELSE DOES?

I HAVE MY REASONS.

NOW I AM GOING OUT. I WANT THE VADAS TO BE READY BY THE TIME I RETURN.

KHANDOBA'S WIFE GROUND THE DAL, PATTED THE PASTE INTO VADAS AND BEGAN TO FRY THEM.

SOON SHE HAD A PLATEFUL OF CRISP, HOT VADAS, READY.

I THINK I'D BETTER TASTE ONE AND SEE.

172

The Moon-god's Messenger

A TALE FROM THE PANCHATANTRA
SCRIPT: B.R.BHAGWAT • ILLUSTRATIONS: V.B.HALBE

A TROOP OF HARES LIVED ON THE SHORES OF A LAKE IN THE MIDDLE OF A FOREST.

THERE WAS PLENTY OF FOOD IN THE FOREST, SO THEY LED A VERY HAPPY LIFE.

THEN ONE DAY, A HERD OF ELEPHANTS CAME BY, IN SEARCH OF WATER.

LOOK! WATER! PLENTY OF IT!

ELEPHANTS! RUN FOR YOUR LIVES!

THAT NIGHT THE FRANTIC HARES HELD A MEETING.

IF WE DON'T DRIVE THOSE BRUTES AWAY SOON, ALL OF US WILL BE KILLED.

COME ON, FRIENDS, LET'S GO AWAY FROM HERE.

THEY'VE GONE! WE'RE SAFE! LONG LIVE VIJAYA!

LOOK THERE HE IS QUIVERING WITH RAGE!

HAVE YOU EVER SEEN HIM SO ANGRY BEFORE?

NO! NEVER!

PLEASE FORGIVE US, O GREAT ONE!

YES, YOUR MAJESTY. PLEASE FORGIVE HIM.